THE WORLD OF CHINESE MYTHS
中国神话世界

Chen Jianing

Yang Yang

陈家宁

杨　阳　编著

Beijing Language and Culture University Press

北京语言学院出版社

Frist Edition 1995

ISBN 7—5619—0414—2/G · 94
Copyright 1995 by Beijing Language and Culture University Press
Published by Beijing Language and Culture University Press
15 Xueyuan Road, Beijing 100083, China
Distributed by China International Book Trading Corporation
35 Chegongzhuang Xilu, P. O. Box 399
Beijing 100044, China
Printed in the People' s Republic of China

女娲补天　　　　　　　　　　　　　毛水仙　画

夸父追日　　　　　　　　　　　　　陈惠冠 画

嫦娥奔月　　　　　　　　　　　　毛水仙　画

tune-telling. They were also found on bamboo strips. Beginning in the 14th and 13th centuries BC, Chinese cast or inscribed characters on bronze to record great historical events. The fragmentary accounts of myths we find now are very brief accounts of the early oral works.

Generally speaking, the writings which can be called books appeared in the Eastern Zhou Dynasty (770—221 BC). They were mainly Confucian classics and classics of other great thinkers and philosophers.

Confucius (551—479 BC) was born in Eastern Zhou Dynasty which was a transitional period from slave society to feudal society. At that time iron was much more widely used than before. As a result, more and better farm and handicraft tools were produced and agriculture and handicraft improved. Economic development brought forth changes in landownership and political structure. Land held by the aristocracy since Western Zhou Dynasty gradually passed to the newly-rising landlord class and peasant class. Politically Western Zhou Dynasty consisted of numerous vassal states. But at the time of Confucius, the more powerful vassals had already extended their domains by military force and were contending with one another for hegemony. At the same time, the authority of the Zhou Dynasty was growing weak. Since the barons of different states were fighting each other for territory, they needed men to advise on government or assist them in their rule. In the time of tumult, many intellectuals studied the art of government to discover ways to enrich the state and strengthen the army. While the art of governing and military strategy and tactics were widely discussed and recorded, no collection of mythic tales made appearance. The fighting for survival did not leave space for romantic mythic tales. Such writings was not needed at the time, nor during the feudal times when Confucianism became orthodoxy. According to one an-

2

cient writer, "In days of old when a sage was on a throne, the official historians wrote records, blind minstrels made songs ..." yet we have no idea what songs the minstrels made. It was also said that the officials at court had collected the gossip of the street which might include early mythic tales, but they were not preserved for later readers. Myths which had no basis in historical fact and ran counter to Confucian tradition were not paid attention to. Only in works by romantic poets like Qu Yuan (340—287 BC) and unconventional scholars like Zhuang Zi (369—286 BC) can we get some idea about the mythology of the primitive society.

From the fragmentary myths available for study today, we can judge a great variety of mythical tales had been in existence. If you explore this remote, mysterious mythical world, you will be surprised by its dazzling beauty and the rich imagination of the primitive people.

It has been my desire to introduce Chinese myths to Western readers. At first I wrote two pieces for a trial, ("Pan Hu, the Dog Which Killed the King's Enemy and Married the Princess", and "Lin Jun, a Tribal Chief Who Killed His Sweet Heart for the People") and found they appealed to Western readers. Then I began in earnest and finished most of the Chinese version when I was attacked by the sinister illness cancer. I felt very sorry that the work had to stop. However, my friends came to help. Liu Ruiling wrote the Chinese version of the second chapter and the first part of the fourth chapter. Yang Yang and E. West did the translation. Li Shizhi made the glossary. In the days when I had the three operations and received the cruel treatment, Yang Yang acted on my behalf in all aspects, matching the English version with the Chinese version and fulfilling the requirements made by the publisher. It is her efforts that made it possible for the book to be published.

While I was writing the Chinese version, I carefully selected best known tales in order to help westerner understand Chinese myths of the primitive society and I also classified them. I rewrote and embellished them according to the material we can find in ancient writing, stringing together smaller pieces of fragments to make larger ones, and if lucky enough into a story. I paid special attention to the original. I hope the collection will be both interesting and informative to western readers.

Chen Jianing

Jan. 19, 1994

4

目　录

第一章　宇宙和人类诞生的神话

一、开天辟地 ……………………………………………（3）

二、太阳 …………………………………………………（7）

三、月亮 …………………………………………………（9）

四、牵牛星和织女星 ……………………………………（12）

五、气象之神 ……………………………………………（15）

六、瑶姬 …………………………………………………（17）

七、夜行游女 ……………………………………………（20）

八、土地之神与土伯 ……………………………………（23）

九、山神与水神 …………………………………………（25）

十、河伯 …………………………………………………（28）

十一、洛神 ………………………………………………（32）

十二、玄珠 ………………………………………………（35）

十三、女娲 ………………………………………………（39）

十四、简狄 ………………………………………………（42）

十五、姜嫄 ………………………………………………（44）

十六、盘瓠 ………………………………………………（47）

十七、廪君 ………………………………………………（54）

第二章　帝王与英雄

一、黄帝与四方天帝 ……………………………………（63）

二、精卫填海 ……………………………………………（66）

三、黄帝与炎帝的战争 …………………………………（68）

5

四、黄帝战蚩尤 …………………………………………（70）

五、猛志常在的刑天 ……………………………………（73）

六、追逐太阳的夸父 ……………………………………（75）

七、为民除害的羿 ………………………………………（77）

八、鲧禹治水 ……………………………………………（85）

第三章　奇异国度

一、大人国 ………………………………………………（91）

二、小人国 ………………………………………………（93）

三、交胫国 ………………………………………………（94）

四、君子国 ………………………………………………（95）

五、轩辕国 ………………………………………………（96）

六、无臂国 ………………………………………………（97）

七、枭阳国 ………………………………………………（98）

八、奇肱国 ………………………………………………（99）

九、三首国 ………………………………………………（101）

十、雨师妾国 ……………………………………………（102）

十一、跂踵国 ……………………………………………（103）

十二、博父国 ……………………………………………（104）

十三、聂耳国 ……………………………………………（105）

十四、一目国 ……………………………………………（106）

十五、长股国 ……………………………………………（108）

十六、一臂国 ……………………………………………（109）

十七、三身国 ……………………………………………（110）

十八、羽民国 ……………………………………………（111）

十九、讙头国 ……………………………………………（112）

二十、厌火国 ……………………………………………（113）

二十一、裸国 ……………………………………………（114）

二十二、贯胸国 …………………………………………（115）

二十三、钉灵国 ……………………………………… (117)

二十四、日林国 ……………………………………… (118)

第四章　异物

一、奇异的动物 ……………………………………… (121)

二、奇草异木 ………………………………………… (129)

第五章　文明创始诸神

一、有巢氏 …………………………………………… (139)

二、燧人氏 …………………………………………… (141)

三、伏羲氏 …………………………………………… (143)

四、神农氏 …………………………………………… (146)

五、方相 ……………………………………………… (150)

六、蚕神 ……………………………………………… (153)

七、船神与车神 ……………………………………… (157)

八、陶神与铜神 ……………………………………… (160)

九、万能之神 ………………………………………… (164)

十、天文之神 ………………………………………… (166)

十一、画神与字神 …………………………………… (169)

十二、音乐与舞蹈之神 ……………………………… (172)

十三、音乐家夔 ……………………………………… (176)

十四、灶神与门神 …………………………………… (180)

附录

总词汇表 ……………………………………………… (187)

CONTENTS

Chapter One Universe and Creation Myths

  1. The Creation of the World: the Separation of Earth and Sky .... (5)

  2. The Sun .... (8)

  3. The Moon .... (10)

  4. Altair and Vega .... (13)

  5. The Gods of Weather .... (16)

  6. Yao Ji, the Goddess Who Helped Da Yu to Control Floods .... (18)

  7. The Wandering Night Goddess .... (21)

  8. The God of the Land and Tu Bo, the God of Death .... (24)

  9. The Gods of Mountains and the Gods of Water .... (26)

10. He Bo, the God of the Yellow River .... (30)

11. The Goddess of the Luo Rriver .... (33)

12. The Black Pearl .... (37)

13. Nü Wa, the Goddess Who Created Humanity .... (40)

14. Jian Di, a Girl Who Became Pregnant After Swallowing a Swallow's Egg .... (43)

15. Jiang Yuan, a Girl Who Gave Birth to a Strange Looking Foetus ... (45)

16. Pan Hu, the Dog Which Killed the King's Enemy and Married the Princess .... (50)

17. Lin Jun, a Tribal Chief Who Killed His Sweet Heart for His People .... (57)

Chapter Two Kings and Heroes

1. Huang Di and the Gods of Four Directions ·················· (64)

2. Jing Wei, a Crow-like Bird Who Wanted to Fill Up the East Sea ······ (67)

3. The War Between Huang Di and Yan Di ·················· (69)

4. Huang Di Fought against Chi You ·················· (71)

5. Xing Tian, a Dead Giant Who Had a Fighting Spirit ·················· (74)

6. Kua Fu, the God Who Intended to Catch the Sun ·················· (76)

7. Yi, the Archer Who Rid Humankind of Evil Monsters ·················· (80)

8. Gun and Da Yu, the Gods Who Controlled the Flood ·················· (87)

Chapter Three　Exotic Lands

1. Land of the Giants ·················· (91)

2. Land of the Dwarfs ·················· (93)

3. The People of Jiao Jing ·················· (94)

4. Jun Zi: the Country of Gentlemen ·················· (95)

5. The Country of Xuan Yuan ·················· (96)

6. The Country of Wu Qi ·················· (97)

7. The Country of Xiao Yang ·················· (98)

8. The Country of Ji Gong ·················· (99)

9. The Country of the Three Heads ·················· (101)

10. The Country of Yu Shi Qie ·················· (102)

11. The Country of Qi Zhong ·················· (103)

12. The Country of Bo Fu ·················· (104)

13. The Country of Nie Er ·················· (105)

14. The Country of Yi Mu, the One-Eyed People ·················· (106)

15. The Country of Chang Gu ·················· (108)

16. The Country of Yi Bi, the One-Armed People ·················· (109)

17. The Country of San Shen, the Triple Bodies ·················· (110)

18. The Country of Yu Min ·················· (111)

19. The Country of Huan Tou ·················· (112)

20. The Country of Yan Huo ·· (113)

21. The Country of Nakedness ··· (114)

22. The Country of Guan Xiong ··· (115)

23. The Country of Ding Ling ··· (117)

24. The Country of Ri Lin ··· (118)

Chapter Four   Strange Creatures

1. Rare Animals ··· (125)

2. Unusual Plants ··· (132)

Chapter Five   Gods of Civilization

1. You Chao, the God Who First Taught People to Build Shelters ······ (140)

2. Sui Ren, Provider of Fire ··· (142)

3. Fu Xi, a Half Man and Half God Who Made Great Contributions to Humankind ··· (144)

4. Shen Nong, the God of Crops and Medicine ······················· (148)

5. Fang Xiang, the God Who Was to Kill the Ghosts of Pestilence ··· (151)

6. The Goddess of Silk ·· (155)

7. The God of Boats and the God of Carts ··························· (158)

8. The God of Pottery and the God of Bronze ······················· (162)

9. Omnipotent Gods ··· (165)

10. The God of Astronomy ·· (167)

11. The God of Paintings and the God of Characters ················· (170)

12. The Gods of Music and Dance ······································ (174)

13. The Musician Kui ··· (178)

14. The Kitchen God and the Door Gods ······························· (183)

Appendix

Glossary ·· (187)

第 一 章
宇宙和人类诞生的神话

CHAPTER ONE

UNIVERSE AND CREATION MYTHS

一、开天辟地

夏夜,当你凝视那群星灿烂,新月如钩的天空时,会不由得想:宇宙究竟有多大?它有边吗?如果有,边在何处?那边缘的外边又是什么?如果没有,它又是如何无极限地延伸的呢?在茫茫的宇宙中谁是主宰?谁又是它的创始者?由于人类认识的限制,这个问题一直未能得到圆满的答复,然而,世界各族都有着关于宇宙创始的神话。

在中国神话中,开辟天地的是盘古。

起初,宇宙是一团浑浑沌沌的大气聚在一起,形状像个硕大无比的鸡蛋。鸡蛋里孕育着一位天神。他的名字叫做盘古。他在这团大气中成长着,昏睡着,一觉就睡了一万八千年。一天,他醒了,睁开眼睛一看,四周黑糊糊的,很觉懊恼烦闷,于是便将手中的斧子一挥,只听一声巨响,鸡蛋破裂开来。那团大气中,轻的部分冉冉上升,成了蔚蓝色的天空,浊而重的部分慢慢下沉,成了黄色的土地。天地分开之后,为了不使它们重新合拢,盘古就头顶青天,脚踏大地,站在天地之间。天每日升高一丈,地每日加厚一丈,盘古也每日长高一丈。这样又过了一万八千年,天高了,地厚了,盘古的身躯也长到了九万里高。他像根长柱子一样撑着天地。又过了许多许多年,他觉得天地不会再合拢了,他也实在太累了,于是便倒下来死去。临死时口中呼出的气变成了风和云;他的声音变成了轰轰的雷霆;左眼变成了太阳,右眼变成了月亮;身躯变为大地和高山;肌肉变为沃土;血液变为江河;筋脉变为道路;须发成了天上明亮的星斗;皮肤和汗毛成了美丽的花草树木,牙齿和骨骼成了坚硬的石头,闪光的金属;骨髓则成了玉石和珍珠。连他的汗水都变成了雨露和甘霖。他的死换来了一个五彩缤纷的世界。

1. The Creation of the World: the Separation of Earth and Sky

During summer nights when we are gazing at the star filled sky and the new moon, we can't help contemplating the vastness of the universe. Does it ever end and if it ever does, where and what is beyond that end? If there is no end, what does infinity look like? Who dominates this endless universe? Who is the creator? Because of humanity's limited understanding, these questions are still unanswered. Despite this, or perhaps because of this, all the world's peoples have creation myths. In Chinese myth, Pan Gu created the world.

In the beginning, the universe was chaos. The atmosphere formed into an enormous egg. Inside the massive egg, the god, Pan Gu, grew. One day, after sleeping for about 18,000 years, he woke up. When he opened his eyes, darkness surrounded him. Dispirited by the blackness, he waved the axe in his hand and with a thundering sound the egg broke. The lighter part of the atmosphere slowly rose, becoming the blue sky. The heavier part sank lowly, becoming the yellow earth. Upon the separation of sky and earth, Pan Gu set foot on the earth and supported the sky with his head, keeping the earth and sky separate. Every day the sky rose one *zhang* (3.3 metres) higher, the earth became one *zhang* thicker, and at the same time, Pan Gu grew one *zhang*. Thus passed another 18,000 years with the sky becoming much higher and the earth much thicker. As the sky expanded, Pan Gu grew to 90,000 *li* (45,000 kilometres). He stood there like a tall pillar, supporting the sky and the earth.

Many many years passed this way, but finally, exhausted, he felt that his support was no longer necessary, thinking that the sky and the earth were forever separated. Exhausted, he died. His dying breath became the winds and clouds, his voice the roaring thunder, his left eye the sun and the right eye the moon. His body formed the four edges of the earth and high mountains. His muscles turned into rich soil and his blood flowed as rivers and lakes. His veins and sinew became roads and his hair became the bright stars in the sky. His skin and fine body hair became beautiful flowers, grass and trees. His teeth and bone became hard stone and glittering metal and his marrow became jade and pearls. Even his sweat became rain drops. Thus, by his death, Pan Gu gave us a colourful world.

二、太 阳

　　在苍茫的大地之东是波涛翻滚的东海,东海之外有座山,山那边又是一片辽阔的海洋,那是海外之海,叫汤谷。那里的海水呈碧绿色,既不咸,也不苦,而是甜丝丝的,带着点香味。那儿有一株并生的树,名叫扶桑。扶桑树高达数千丈,粗一千余围,两两同根,相依而生,叶子有六七尺宽,树上还结着紫红色的桑葚。金蚕卧在树上,玉鸡栖于树顶,在黎明到来时,它便振翅鸣叫。这儿便是太阳居住的地方。起初,天上有十个太阳,九个栖息在下枝,一个太阳高高挂在上枝。太阳们还常常在碧水中沐浴。它们的母亲名叫羲和,是天帝俊的妻子。这十个太阳轮番出没在天空,驾着六条龙,乘着车子,从东往西奔驰,而赶车的便是妈妈羲和。一天,十轮太阳一齐跑出来了,在天空自由自在地游荡,它们炙烤着大地,毁掉了地球上的生物,于是善射的羿射下了其中的九个太阳,从此天上就剩下一个太阳,它的光和热足够温暖大地人间了。

2. The Sun

To the east of the boundless earth was the roaring East China sea beyond which was a mountain, and even further beyond this was another large sea, Tang Gu. Its dark green sea water was never salty or bitter, but sweet and fragrant. There grew the two trunked tree, Fu Sang, several thousand *zhang* (1 *zhang* = 3.3 metres) high and several hundred *zhang* thick. The leaves were six or seven *chi* (2 metres) wide. Myriads of purple mulberries and a gold silk worm grew on the tree while a jade rooster rested on the top, greeting each dawn by flapping its wings and crowing.

Here, where the sun lived, ten suns used to inhabit the sky. Nine rested on the lower branches while only one claimed the top branch. These suns often bathed in the sea water. Driven by their mother, Xi He, a wife of Di Jun, the King of Heaven, they often took turns riding a chariot driven by six dragons, running along the fixed celestial orbit from east to west. One day, instead of coming out one at a time as they usually did, these ten suns together roamed the sky, scorching the earth as they went, ruining every living earthly thing in their path. So later Yi, an excellent marksman, shot nine of them, leaving one sun to light and heat the entire world and all of humanity perfectly.

三、月 亮

　　每当农历的十五，一轮光辉的明月便会升向天空。虽然它像玉盘一样晶莹，中间却有暗影婆娑。在中国，古时就有人指出那是月中山河的影子，其空处则为海水影。然而更多的人却对着美丽的月亮编织着一个又一个动人的神话。古人说天上共有十二个月亮。他们也常常驾着车子在天空遨游。它们的母亲也是帝俊的妻子，名叫常羲。她常常给她的月亮孩子们洗浴。也有人说月亮中有一只癞蛤蟆，而这只癞蛤蟆却是一位美丽的神女变的，她的名字叫姮娥，即我们今天所说的嫦娥。嫦娥的丈夫便是射九日的羿。羿很爱自己的妻子。为了与她永为夫妻，羿去西王母处讨了不死之药。西王母是个豹尾虎牙，掌管瘟疫刑罚的怪神。她头发乱蓬蓬的，戴着一只玉胜，还常常叫啸。有三只青鸟替她觅食，还有一保三足乌做她的仆从。她住的昆仑山有弱水环绕。若想渡过弱水非乘龙不可。昆仑的外面还环绕着大火熊熊的火炎山，无论什么东西到这里都会燃烧。羿冲破水火的包围，千辛万苦地来到西王母处。西王母虽然长相凶恶，却很理解羿的心情，于是很慷慨地把不死之药给了他。羿高高兴兴地回到家中把药拿给妻子看，并说今后他们可以永不分离。他万万没想到嫦娥背着他独自把药吃了。药刚一下肚，奇怪的事就发生了。她的身子飘飘上升，离开了地面。脚下是灰茫茫的大地，头上是湛蓝的天空。天上皓月当空。嫦娥一直飞到月亮上。谁想到她刚一踏上月球，身上便长出许多疙瘩，嘴变大了，肚子也鼓了起来。就这样，一位美丽的神女变成了一只癞蛤蟆。也有人说她没有变成蛤蟆，只是在月中感到非常寂寞。尽管月中有玉楼金宫，也无法使她解脱对丈夫的思念之情。

9

3. The Moon

On the fifteenth day of every lunar month, a bright moon shows its full face. Though it is as clear as a jade plate, we can still discern some dark shadows. According to people in ancient China, they were the shadows of mountains and rivers and the clear space was the shadow of the seas. Still others created many moving myths about the beautiful moon. Ancient people said that twelve moons used to live in the sky and often roamed about in a chariot. Chang Xi, their mother and another of Di Jun's wives, often bathed her moon children. Others said that in the moon lived a toad; the beautiful goddess, Heng E, today called Chang E, turned into this toad.

Chang E's husband, Yi who shot down the nine suns, loved his wife deeply. In order to be with her forever, he went to the Queen Mother of the West, the goddess in charge of disease and punishment, asking for the elixir of immortality. The Queen Mother of the West was a strange looking goddess; her hair was messy and she wore a jade earring, she had a leopard's tail and a tiger's teeth. She often shouted. Three green birds searched for her food and a three-footed crow worked as her servant. She lived on Mount Kunlun which was surrounded by the Ruo River, a river which could only be crossed with the assistance of a dragon. Mount Kunlun was surrounded by a ring of flaming mountains, so that anybody trying to reach it risked being burned. Yi managed to get across the Ruo River and through the flames, finally meeting the Queen Mother of the West.

Although she looked very fierce, the Queen Mother of the West was very understanding and generously gave Yi the elixir. Yi returned home happily and showed the medicine to his wife saying that they would be together forever. However, unknown to Yi, Chang E took all the medicine. As soon as she swallowed it something strange happened. Her body grew light and she was lifted off the ground. Under her feet was the grey earth and above her head was the blue sky. In the sky was a bright moon, so Chang E flew straight to it, yet the moment she set foot there, she developed many lumps; her mouth grew and her body swelled. And so a beautiful goddess was transformed into a toad.

Still others said she didn't turn into a toad at all, but said instead that she was merely excruciatingly lonely in the moon. Even though there was a beautiful palace there, she simply couldn't live without longing for her husband.

四、牵牛星和织女星

　　夏夜的星空，有一条白茫茫的长带，西方人称它为牛奶路，我们的古人把它叫做天河或银河。天河的东面有一个由四颗星星组成的星座，那便是织女星；天河的西面有三颗星星形成一条直线，那是牵牛星。织女星是天帝的外孙女，她是个既美丽又温柔的姑娘。她天天都在纺纱织布，织成又轻又薄云雾般的绸缎，终日劳作不息，没有时间梳妆打扮，生活中很少有欢娱的时间。天帝见她既孤独又辛劳，便把她嫁给天河西边的牛郎。婚后两人的生活非常美满，他们形影不离地在天上游玩，在银河旁嬉戏。织女从此只贪恋夫妻的恩爱，从而荒废了纺织。于是天帝便生起气来，把他们叫来，责备一番之后，让她回到河东去，只许他们夫妻一年相会一次。

　　回到河东以后，织女又开始过那寂寞而辛劳的生活了。她挥动着柔嫩、纤细的双手，用梭子扎扎地织着绸子，然而一天竟织不出一匹，整天泪水洗面；天河西边的牛郎也无心耕作，整日价来来回回地徘徊。

　　天河又清又浅，然而他们夫妻却无法交谈，只是含情相对。农历七月七日的夜晚，夫妻相会的日子终于来临。这一夕，牵牛星和织女星光芒四射，无数的喜鹊从四面八方飞来。它们在天河上织成了一座鹊桥，让织女从上走过。她身着盛装，迈着轻盈的步子，走过鹊桥回到丈夫身边。

4. Altair and Vega

In the sky during the summer nights you can find a long white band; people in the West call it the Milky Way, but ancient people in China called it Tian He, the Heavenly River, or Yin He, the Silvery Way. To the east of Tian He is a constellation consisting of four stars, called Vega. To the west three stars, called Altair, form a straight line.

The beautiful and gentle Vega, a granddaughter of the King of Heaven, wove silk and satin every day. She worked so hard that she had no time to enjoy herself. Realizing that she was hardworking but lonely, the King of Heaven married her to Altair to the west of the Heavenly River. After they were married, they lived very happily, romping in the sky together and enjoying themselves beside the Silvery Way.

The previously hardworking Vega now devoted all her time to her new love, making the King of Heaven very angry. After summoning and blaming the two lovers, he demanded that Vega return to the east of the river allowing her to meet Altair but once a year. After returning to the east of the river, Vega resumed her lonely and tiring work. Waving her thin and delicate hands back and forth, she wove silk and satin, but because she was always sad and tearful, she was unable to weave even one bolt per day. Altair, to the west of the Heavenly River, couldn't plow the fields either; he just moped about each day thinking only of Vega.

Although the river was clear and shallow, the couple could not talk to each other across it. They could only look longingly at one another.

Finally on the seventh night of the seventh lunar month, Vega and Altair could be together at last. On this day they shone brilliantly. Magpies flew from afar creating a bridge over the Silvery River so Vega could walk across to meet her husband. Vega, beautifully dressed, hurried across the magpie bridge to return to her husband.

五、气象之神

在中国神话中有众多的风、云、雷、雨之神。有一位著名的风神叫穷奇。他是刮广莫风的,形状像只长着翅膀的老虎。他同时还能驱逐妖邪。妖邪一看到丑陋的穷奇便四处逃窜。飞廉被一些人认为是风神的首领。他的长相更怪:脑袋像麻雀而有角,身体像鹿却又长着蛇的尾巴与豹的花纹。雨神的首领名叫妾。她浑身黑色,长着人一样的面孔,左耳有青蛇,右耳有赤蛇。两手还各拿着一条蛇。也有人说她拿着的是龟。殷人便常常祭祀她并向她问卜。

夔是雷神,他住在东海的流波山上。他像只苍牛,但是没长角。也有人说他像龙而有角,身上的鳞甲像日月那样闪着光。古时,打雷的声音被认为是天鼓,夔也被认为与音乐有关系。云神住在神宫里,她常常乘着龙驾的车子周游四方。她为楚人所祀奉。

5. The Gods of Weather

In Chinese myths there are many gods of wind, cloud, thunder and rain. Qiong Qi, a famous god of wind, blowing north wind and resembling a tiger with wings, could get rid of evil monsters. Whenever monsters saw this ugly god they just tried to run away. Fei Lian, even more strange looking than Qiong Qi, was regarded as the head of the wind gods. His head was like a sparrow with horns. His body, shaped like a deer with the spots of a leopard, had a snake's tail.

The head of the rain gods, Qie, was completely black. She had the face of a man and on her left ear hung a green snake and on the right ear hung a red snake. Some said she held a snake in each hand but others said it was a turtle. People of Yin clan often offered her sacrifices and asked her to foretell their future.

Kui, the God of Thunder, lived on Mount Liu Bo on the East China Sea. According to some, he looked like an old hornless ox while to others like a horned dragon with a scaly body glistening like the sun and the moon. In ancient times, thunder was thought to be the drums of heaven so the god, Kui, is often associated with music.

Now the Goddess of Clouds lived in the heavenly palace. She often rode in the chariot driven by dragons and roamed about in the sky. She was worshipped by the Chu people.

六、瑶　姬

　　在巍峨苍郁的巫山南面，住着一位美丽的女神，名叫瑶姬。她夭折之后，被封为巫山的云雨之神。她光彩照人，仪态万方，早晨化做一片美丽的朝云，晚上又变做一阵潇潇的暮雨。据说战国末年的楚怀王就梦见过她，诗人宋玉听到了这事，还作了赋来歌颂她，后来民间还流传着这样的故事。

　　瑶姬不但美丽，而且善良。当年中国洪水泛滥，大禹率领几万民工治理九州水患，就住在巫山之下。有一天，狂风骤起，悬崖震荡，山谷崩塌，乱石纷飞，工程无法进行下去。这时瑶姬正从东海遨游回来到了巫山，大禹就请瑶姬帮忙。在她的帮助下，顺利地凿通了巫峡，江水畅流东去。之后，大禹爬到巫山上向她道谢，然而发现她已化为石头。而那石头又突然散做轻云，又变成夕雨，甚至变成飞翔的白鹤或游龙，千万变化，永无定形。当大禹再度谒访时，这时山中出现了琼楼玉宇，瑶姬端坐台上，正式接见了他。瑶姬让侍女取来一只小匣子，把匣子里装的治水的仙书交给大禹，还让她的属神协同大禹继续治水。有了她的帮助，大禹终于将横流十数年的洪水治平。

　　从此以后，瑶姬便在巫山留住下来，天天关切着三峡中的行船。如有船只在巫山通过，就派神鸦迎送，以保行船的安全。瑶姬由于长久地站在高崖眺望，后来便化做一座山峰，就是有名的神女峰；她的侍女们随后也变成大大小小的峰峦，就是现在的巫山十二峰。

6. Yao Ji, the Goddess Who Helped Da Yu to Control Floods

To the south of the huge and verdant green Mount Wu, lived a beautiful goddess, Yao Ji. After she died, she became the goddess of clouds and rain on Mount Wu. She was lovely, poised and graceful. In the morning, she turned into beautiful morning clouds whereas in the evening she became soft gentle evening rain. It is said that during the last years of the Warring States, Huai, King of Chu state dreamed about her. The poet, Song Yu, heard about this and wrote a poetic essay in praise of her, so her legend lives on.

Yao Ji was not only beautiful but also kind. At that time, huge floods often ravaged China. Da Yu, who lived under the foot of Mount Wu, led thousands of laborers to control the flood. One day, cliffs and valleys collapsed because strong winds had suddenly sprung up. Many stones were flung up so that people simply couldn't go on with their work. At that time Yao Ji had just returned to Mount Wu from the East Sea so Da Yu asked her for help. With her help, the laborers chiseled smoothly through the Wu Gorge allowing the river to flow to the east. Then Da Yu climbed up Mount Wu to thank her, only to find she had turned to stone. Suddenly the stone turned to light clouds, then to gentle rain and finally flying cranes, dragons and various other shapes.

18

And when Da Yu went to meet Yao Ji again, he found her in some beautiful palaces on the mountain. After receiving him, Yao Ji asked the maid to fetch a small box containing a book about controlling floods. She gave the book to Da Yu and asked one of her gods to help him continue the work. With her help, Da Yu was finally able to control the flood raging more than ten years.

From then on, Yao Ji lived on Mount Wu watching over the passing boats on the Three Gorges. Whenever some boats or ships passed by Mount Wu, she would send a magic crow to protect them. After many years of watching boats and people from her mountain peak, she turned into the famous Goddess Peak and her maids were transformed into ridges and peaks of various sizes, altogether making up the twelve peaks of Mount Wu.

七、夜行游女

夜幕降临了，鸟儿归林了，母亲们把孩子们叫回家，不许他们再出门玩耍，因为夜行游女就要出来了。

夜行游女披上羽毛，就变成了飞鸟。它在人们的屋顶上空盘旋；下落时脱下羽毛，就变成了袒露着两个乳房的年轻妇人。

有人说她是天帝的女儿。也有人说她曾是个年轻的母亲。她非常喜欢孩子，更想要一个自己的孩子。怀孕之后，她天天盼着孩子降生，而且给未出世的婴儿做了许多小衣服。可是后来她竟然因难产而死了，死后就变成夜行游女。她在人们的屋前徘徊着，听着屋内孩子们的嬉笑声和老祖母给孩子们讲故事的声音；她从窗缝儿和门缝儿里窥探着，总想伺机偷走人家的孩子。她看中哪家的孩子，就把她的羽毛放在他的衣服上，或把血滴在上面做记号，以便将来把他偷走。妈妈们知道她的计谋之后，一到天黑，便连孩子们衣服也不往外面晾了。

夜行游女夜夜在一家又一家的庭院中游荡，可是一个孩子也没有能够偷成。在天色即将发亮的时候，她便披上羽毛，化做一只飞鸟快快地飞走了。

7. The Wandering Night Goddess

When night fell and birds returned to the woods, mothers would call their children home, not allowing them to play outside because the Wandering Night Goddess would emerge. When the goddess wore her feathers, she would become a bird, flying above people's roofs. When she landed she took off her feathers to become a bare-chested young woman. Some people said that she was the daughter of the King of Heaven while others said that she used to be a young mother.

She loved children very much and was eager to have a child of her own. Once she became pregnant; with each passing day, she looked forward to the birth of her child and made many baby dresses in anticipation. Sadly though, she died in childbirth and after her death became the Wandering Night Goddess. She always lingered in front of people's houses, listening to the laughter inside and the voices of the grandmothers telling stories to their grand-children. She peeped through the cracks in the doors and looked through windows hoping to steal away some children. If she saw a child she liked, she would identify him by putting some feathers on his clothes or by dropping blood on his clothes so she could steal away the child later. When mothers uncovered her plot, they dared not put their children's clothes outside at nightfall. The goddess roamed in the courtyards of one household after another but couldn't steal even one child, so when dawn came she would put on her feathers, once again become a bird and fly sadly away.

八、土地之神与土伯

　　大地是多么美丽呵！荒原上到处芳草萋萋，开遍了黄色的、白色的野花，爬满了蓝色的和粉色的牵牛。鱼儿在清浅的河水里游来游去。鸟儿在大树上筑巢孵化小鸟。人们热爱大地，崇拜大地。上古的人用酒、人血和牲畜的血洒在地上礼拜大地。后来他们把土地之神尊为社神。神话中的社神很多，他们是土地之主，生育庄稼和万物。然而，有生就有死。人们畏惧死亡，于是神话中又出现了索取人命的死亡之神——土伯。土伯看守幽都的大门。幽都便是地下的幽冥世界。那儿到处都是黑漆漆的，看不见太阳和月亮的光辉，只有青色的鬼火偶尔闪烁一下。那里有黑鸟、黑蛇、黑豹、黑虎、和长着蓬松尾巴的黑狐狸。那里还有座大黑山，山上出没的都是些黑人。土伯本身的形象也十分可怕。他的头像老虎，长着三只眼睛，身体像牛，脊背的肉隆起，手爪鲜血淋淋，拿着很多根绳子，飞奔着追逐人们。他的恶相足以表现人们对死亡的恐惧。

8. The God of the Land and Tu Bo, the God of Death

How beautiful the land was with fragrant grass everywhere! Many yellow and white wild flowers and pink and blue morning glory covered the land. Fish swam about in the clear and shallow river water and birds built their nests on the trees preparing for their young. The ancient people loved and worshipped their land, sprinkling wine, the blood of people and livestock in worship. Later they worshipped the gods in charge of their land.

There are many gods of the land in Chinese myth. They owned the land and were in charge of grains and all plants. However, life also means death and since people are afraid of death so in the myths appeared the God of Death, Tu Bo, who took away people's lives. He kept guard over the completely dark underworld where it was impossible to see the sun or the moon. Only occasionally could anyone see the glistening of the will-o'-the-wisp. Black birds, black snakes, black leopards, black tigers and even fluffy-tailed black foxes inhabited this bleak underworld. There was also a large black mountain inhabited by black people. Tu Bo looked very fierce with his tiger's head and three eyes; the back of his oxen-like body was swollen with muscles. Holding a number of ropes in his bloody hands, he ran after people. His fierce appearance itself showed people's fear of death.

九、山神与水神

  上古的人民认为山有山神，水有水神，在中国神话世界里有许多长相奇怪的山神。羸母山的山神长着豹一样的尾巴；衡山的山神牛身马尾，长着两个脑袋八只脚，人们说它出现在哪里，哪里就有兵灾。钟山之神长着人一样的面孔，蛇一样的身子，浑身通红。他睁开眼世界就是白昼，闭上眼就是黑夜，一吹气就是冬天，一呼气就是夏天。中国最高的山是喜玛拉雅山，不过古人最推崇的还是昆仑山。昆仑山神，人面虎身，尾巴上白斑点点。在中国的东方，有一座雄伟的苍山，那就是人们可景仰的泰山。泰山之神治理鬼，人死之后，灵魂都归于泰山。有人说泰山之神是天帝的孙子，呼唤他，可以消除疾病。

  古人认为我国四面都是波涛翻滚的大海。在东海的岛上住着一位大神。他是黄帝的儿子，名叫禺虢。他长着人面鸟身，耳上挂着两条黄蛇，脚下还踩着两条黄蛇。北海之神禺京又是禺虢的儿子。南海的海神半挂两条青蛇，脚踩两条赤蛇，名叫不廷胡余。西海之神人面鸟躯，也是耳挂两条青蛇，脚踩两条赤蛇，名叫弇兹。

  长江和洞庭湖常常为古人赞诵。在长江一带的水域里常见有两位女神游玩。她们妍媚冶艳，异于常人。她们是天帝的两个女儿，住在烟波浩淼的洞庭湖。她们常常伴着飘风与浓雨出现。

9. The Gods of Mountains and the Gods of Water

People in ancient times believed that mountains had mountain gods and the water water gods. Many strange looking mountain gods abound in the world of Chinese myth. The Mountain God of Mount Luo Mu had the tail of a leopard, and the God of Mount Heng the body of an ox, the tail of a horse, two heads and eight feet. People said that wherever he went war would break out. The red-skinned God of Mount Zhong had the face of a human being and the body of a snake. When he opened his eyes, daylight filled the world and when he closed his eyes, night fell. When he puffed air, winter began and when he breathed out, summer arrived.

Even though the Himalayas were the highest mountains in China, Mount Kunlun was the mountain that ancient people worshipped the most. The God of Mount Kunlun had a human face but a tiger's body and a white spotted tail.

The mountain most admired in the east was the massive Tai Shan. The God of Mount Tai was in charge of ghosts or spirits. When people died, their spirits returned to Mount Tai. It is said that the God of Mount Tai was the grandson of the King of Heaven and calling him could help one get rid of disease.

Ancient people thought that China was surrounded by a roaring sea and on an island in the East Sea lived the god, Yu Hao. The son of Huang Di, he had the face of a human, the body of a bird, and two yellow snakes on his ears and under his feet. The God of the North Sea, Yu Jing, was the son of Yu Hao. The God of the South Sea, Bu Ting Hu Yu, had two green snakes on his ears and two red snakes under his feet. The God of the West Sea, Yan Ci, had the face of a human, the body of a bird, two green snakes on his ears and two red snakes attached to his feet.

The Yangtse River and Dongting Lake were highly praised by the ancient people. In the water of the Yangtse, one could often see two extremely delicate and charming goddesses, two daughters of the King of Heaven who were living in the mist and ripples of Dongting Lake. They often appeared along with the wind and rain.

十、河 伯

河伯

河伯是黄河的水神，名叫冰夷，又叫冯夷。他的下身长得如同鱼，而上身却是个美男子。猪婆龙是他的使者，鳖是他的从事。乌贼鱼充当他的小吏。河伯统帅四月百川而称王。就连他的属下都很威风，出外替河伯办事要骑上白马，并带着十二个小孩子做随从。

河伯常常驾着两条龙，乘着云车，在升腾的云雾中遨游。也常常带着美女在河边游玩。传说中的河伯是个贪财的小人。如果有人带着贵重的东西过河，他便兴风作浪，覆没船只，以便抢掠财物。一次，他碰到了个名叫澹台子羽的肝胆男儿。澹台子羽带着一块价值连城的璧玉渡河，河伯得知此事后便起了贪心，非要弄到手不可。于是便派了大神阳侯掀起滔天大浪，又叫两条蛟龙去弄翻他的船只。然而澹台子羽却毫无惧色。他站在颠簸的船头，拔出宝剑将凶猛不可一世的蛟龙杀死。他的船乘风破浪渡过河之后，便转过身来，把那块璧玉往河中一丢，并用鄙夷不屑的口吻说："河伯，你要是想要这块玉就拿去吧！"这时河伯跳出水面接住了那块璧玉，然而接着又弹回澹台子羽的手中。澹台子羽又将那块玉扔进河里，接连三次玉都被弹了回来。澹台子羽明白连厚颜无耻的河伯也无法承受这种羞辱了，于是便把玉砸了个粉碎扬长而去，以表示他杀死蛟龙并不是为了惜财，而是不屈服于暴力。

10. He Bo, the God of the Yellow River

He Bo or Bing Yi, in charge of many rivers, was the God of the Yellow River. The lower part of his body was like a fish but the upper part was that of a handsome man. Zhu Po Long, today called crocodile was his servant and a soft shelled turtle was his subordinate. An ink fish was his official. He Bo was in charge of all the rivers. Even his subordinates were very imposing. Those who ran errands would ride on white horses with twelve children as their servants. He Bo often rode playfully through the clouds on a chariot driven by two dragons. He also often played with beautiful goddesses along the river bank.

He Bo was said to be a greedy villain. If some people passed by the river with something precious, he would stir up a storm to overturn the boats so he could rob them. One day he met the brave young man called Tantai Zi Yu, who wanted to cross the river. Tantai Zi Yu was carrying priceless jade. Knowing this, He Bo wanted to get it, so he sent the god, Yang Hou, to stir up a big storm and two dragons to capsize his ship and his boats. Yet Tantai Zi Yu was not afraid at all. He stood on the pulsing bow of the boat, took out his sword and killed the fierce dragons. After his boat got through the storm and crossed the river, he turned back and threw the jade into the river, saying scornfully to He Bo, "He Bo, take the jade if you want." Then He Bo jumped out of the water, caught the jade and made it bounce back into Tantai Zi Yu's hands. Tantai Zi Yu just threw the jade into the river again but He Bo bounced it back several times, so Tantai Zi Yu realized that even shameless He Bo could not bear such an insult so he smashed the jade and walked away with his head held high. In doing this, he showed that he killed the dragons not for the treasure but simply to resist He Bo's use of force.

十一、洛　神

　　在银波粼粼的洛水之上,有一位美丽的女神。她体态窈窕,行步婀娜多姿,面颊润如出水芙蓉,眼睛流盼而多情。据说她是伏羲氏的女儿,在洛水中溺死后成为洛神。人们也称她为宓妃。她的丈夫便是黄河之神河伯。与丈夫成婚后,一度夫妻和美,过着甜蜜幸福的生活。他们同乘一辆车子,乘风破浪在黄河上游玩;他们的车子由龙和螭驾驶,车盖由荷叶制成,车子还可以离开水面,驶上昆仑山巅。他们在水中的家,是座瑰丽华美的宫殿。宫殿的顶部由鱼鳞覆盖,角楼由紫贝雕成。堂上绘着彩龙,厅堂漆为朱红。然而英俊的河伯却品行不端,这使得宓妃愁苦万分。

　　一天,她和女伴们到洛水之滨玩耍,那是一群快活天真的女仙。她们有的在浅滩上采集灵芝,有的拿着从蚌壳中取出的明珠在碧波上行走,有的在采集翠鸟的羽毛……,只有她落落寡欢地站在岩石边上,看上去是那么惆怅,那么忧伤。正在这时,她遇到了射日的羿,于是一见钟情,与这位不得志的英雄相爱了。她的丈夫河伯发现这事之后,非常气恼,他便化为一条白龙游到水边去窥探。正巧羿发现了他,便弯弓发箭,射瞎了他的左眼。河伯到天帝那里告状,并请天帝为他做主,杀死后羿。

　　天帝问道:"羿为什么要射你呢?"

　　河伯回答说:"我化做白龙在水中游玩。"

　　天帝对品行不端的河伯是不偏袒的。他说:"你要是安分守己地做神,羿怎么会侵犯你呢? 你自己变成了兽,他当然可以射你。我看羿是没有过错的。"

　　据说后来宓妃与后羿终于结成了夫妻。

11. The Goddess of the Luo River

In the silvery water of the Luo River lived a beautiful and graceful goddess with beautiful eyes and a face as exquisite as a hibiscus. She was originally said to be the daughter of Fu Xi. She drowned and thus became the goddess of the Luo River. People also called her Fu Fei. Her husband was He Bo, the God of the Yellow River. After they got married they lived very happily for some time. They often rode in the chariot and played in the Yellow River. Their chariot was drawn by dragons and the cover was made of lotus leaves. The chariot could also fly over the surface of the water and even fly to the top of Mount Kunlun. Their home in the water was a magnificent palace with a roof of scales and a corner tower made of purple shells. The palace was painted with colorful dragons and the halls were painted red. However, the handsome He Bo was ill behaved which upset Fu Fei very much.

One day she went to the banks of the Luo River with her beautiful and lively companions. Some of them were collecting glossy ganoderma along the shore and some, carrying pearls in their hands, were walking on the silvery water and some were collecting kingfisher feathers...; only she herself was standing dejectedly beside the rock. She looked very upset. Just then she met Yi who shot down the nine suns. She and this hero fell in love at first sight. When her husband, He Bo, learned this he was very angry so he turned himself into a white dragon and swam to the riverside to watch them. Yi happened to see him, took out his bow and arrow and shot him in his left eye and blinded him. He Bo complained to the King of Heaven and asked him to punish Yi and kill him.

Then the King of Heaven asked him, "Why did Yi want to shoot you?"

He Bo answered, "Because I turned myself into a white dragon and played in the water."

The King of Heaven was not in favor of the ill behaved He Bo, so he said, "If you were a good god, why would Yi shoot you? Since you behaved like a beast, Yi shot you. In my opinion, he shouldn't be blamed."

It was said that later Fu Fei and Yi became a couple at last.

十二、玄　珠

　　黄帝是天上的大神,也是人间的帝王。他经常从天上到地下来游玩。他在昆仑山上有一座巍峨壮丽的宫殿。宫殿里有珠树、瑶树等许多生长珍珠和美玉的树,其中一株叫琅玕树。琅玕树上的美玉极其宝贵,所以黄帝派了三头六目的天神离朱去看守。离朱的三个脑袋轮流睡觉又轮流醒来,他的眼睛能看到百步之外针尖大的东西。所以就是有通天本领的人也休想偷走琅玕树上的玉。尽管黄帝有许多珠宝,他最喜欢的还是一颗又黑又亮的宝珠——玄珠,并常常把它握在手中玩弄。一天,黄帝又要到昆仑山去。在路过赤水时把玄珠掉进水里了,于是他便让离朱去寻找。离朱六只眼睛都睁大也没有看见珠子的踪影,黄帝又让攫掇去找,因为攫掇不但眼神好,手脚也快,如果珠子被水流冲走,他一定能跑着捞回来。然而攫掇在水下找了很久,最后还是两手空空地上了岸。黄帝正不知如何是好,象罔向前说道:"要不然就让我试试吧!"

　　共实象罔并没有什么特殊的本领,他只不过想撞撞大运。因为连离朱和攫掇都没找到宝珠,他若失败了也不丢什么身份。然而,没想到他一下水就觉得脚下有什么滑腻的东西,蹲下身一摸,恰恰是那颗珠子。于是他便欢欢喜喜地上岸将宝珠交给了黄帝。黄帝拿着珠子笑了,他说:

　　"奇怪,这珠子谁都找不到,怎么会叫象罔找到了呢?既然他有超人的本领,宝珠就由他替我保管吧。"

　　象罔本是个迷迷糊糊的人,找到宝珠之后,他非常得意,于是变得更加漫不经心了。结果珠子很快又不见了,这次是给震蒙氏的一个女子偷去了。

黄帝得知这事之后非常气恼,于是派天神去擒拿她。那女子这时才害了怕。惊慌之余,她把珠子吞进肚里跳进了汶川。死后她成了汶川的水神。她的死毕竟是自己的过错造成的,所以她变成了马头龙身的怪样子。从那以后黄帝也永远失去了那颗黑宝珠。

12. The Black Pearl

Huang Di was not only the God of Heaven but also the King of the World. He often left Heaven to play on Earth. In his magnificent palace on Mount Kunlun, pearl and jade trees grew. The jade on one tree called Lang Gan was so priceless that Huang Di sent the god, Li Zhu, who had three heads and six eyes, to watch the tree. Li Zhu's three heads slept and woke up by turns. He could see tiny things like the eye of a needle more than a hundred paces away. So even if one were very powerful and skillful, the jade could not be stolen from the tree. Even though Huang Di had a great deal of jewellery, the piece he liked best was a bright black pearl. He often fondled it in his hand.

One day, on his way to Mount Kunlun, as Huang Di was passing the Chi Shui River, the pearl happened to fall into the water. He sent Li Zhu to look for it, but even Li Zhu's six eyes couldn't see any sign of the pearl. Then Huang Di asked Jue Duo to look for it. Because Jue Duo not only had sharp eyesight but also hands of great speed and desterity, so if the pearl was swept away by the river, he would be fast enough to get it back. However, Jue Fuo searched the water for a long time and came up empty-handed. Huang Di was at a loss what to do when Xiang Wang came to him and said, "Let me have a try."

Xiang Wang had no special power or skill at all. He just wanted to try his luck because even Li Zhu and Jue Duo failed to find the pearl so he would lose nothing by trying to find it. To his surprise the moment he was in the water, he felt something smooth under his feet. When he crouched down and felt it he found the pearl, so he carried it happily to the bank and gave it to Huang Di. Huang Di took the pearl and, all smiles again, said, "I wonder why Xiang Wang could find the pearl but everybody else failed to do so. Now that you have such an unusual skill you may be in charge of it for me."

However, Xiang Wang was a careless person. After he found the pearl he became very proud and even more careless and so the pearl disappeared very soon. This time it was stolen by a girl of Zhen Meng family. Huang Di became very angry upon learning this so he sent the gods of heaven to catch her. The lady swallowed the pearl in fright and jumped into the Wen River. After her death she became the goddess of the Wen River. After all, her death was her own fault, so she was turned into a strange looking goddess with the head of a horse and the body of a dragon. From then on Huang Di lost forever the black pearl.

十三、女　娲

天地开辟的时候，没有人类。在中国神话中，人类是女娲创造的。

女娲是位远古的女神。她的母亲是广袤的大地。她长着人一样的上体，蛇一样的下身。女娲在造人类之前，先造了十个神祇。然后她在正月初一那天造了鸡，初二造狗，初三造羊，初四造猪，初五造牛，初六造马，到了初七这天，便开始造人。

女娲把黄土分成小团儿捏人，捏累了，便用一根绳子在泥里甩起来，于是泥点飞溅，纷纷落了下来，都变成了人。后来她又给她的人类儿女们规定了婚姻制度，让他们去生育繁衍，所以后人又把她奉为婚姻之神，并为她建了庙宇祭祀她，每当二月，在万物竞萌之际，青年男女便到她的庙前游乐，然后情侣们双双到树丛或其它幽僻的地方完婚。他们既不要像我们今天那样履行什么法律手续，也不举行什么重大仪式。她的儿女们就这样欢欢快快地生活着。

可是，有一天大难降临在他们的头上。古时候，人们认为天是圆的，地是方的。天是由四根大柱擎持着，大地是由四根大绳拉拽着。这时，天柱突然折断，地绳也骤然断绝。于是天崩地裂，大火熊熊燃起，洪水浩浩奔流，凶猛的野兽，四处乱窜。女娲心里非常难受，为了解救万民的痛苦，她便砍下了神龟的四脚做为擎天的柱子，熔炼五色的石头去补苍天，她填塞了洪水，诛灭了野兽，于是人类又重新过上了正常的生活。之后，她乘着雷车，驾着龙和青虬，坐在美丽的车垫上，在缭绕的瑞云上升上了九重天。

13. Nü Wa, the Goddess Who Created Humanity

When the sky and the earth were separated, people did not yet exist. In Chinese myth, humanity was created by the goddess, Nü Wa, daughter of the boundless earth. Her upper body was just like a human's and her lower body was just like a snake. Before Nü Wa made human beings, she first made ten gods. Then on the first day of the Lunar New Year, she created a rooster and on the second day, the dog and on the third, a sheep, on the fourth, a pig, on the fifth, an ox, on the sixth, a horse and when it came to the seventh, she started to make human beings.

Nü Wa divided the yellow earth into different types of clay and fashioned clay figures from it. When she got tired, she just dipped a long rope in the mud, waving it everywhere. Each moulded clay figure and each splash of mud which fell from the rope became a human being. Once she had peopled the earth, she created marriage customs, providing her human children the means to create later generations. This is why people regarded her as the Goddess of Marriage and built temples to worship her. Whenever the second month arrived and all living things were about to blossom, young men and women would play in front of her temple. Lovers would go into the woods or some other quiet places to get married, using neither laws nor ceremonies. Her children lived happily this way.

However, one day a massive disaster befell them. In ancient times, people thought the sky was round and the earth was square. The sky was propped up by four large pillars and the earth was pulled by four long ropes. One day the pillars and the earth's ropes suddenly broke. With a great crash on Earth, the sky collapsed. Floods raged and fierce wild beasts ran around everywhere. On seeing this, Nü Wa was greatly saddened. In order to set human beings free from all this suffering, she cut off the four legs of an extraodinarily powerful turtle to be the pillars supporting the sky. She melted down coloured stones and used the resulting substance to fill in the fragmented sky. She controlled the floods and rid the land of the wild beasts so that human beings could resume their normal life. Then, she rode the thunder chariot drawn by dragons. She sat on the beautiful mat of the chariot and rose to the ninth heaven, the highest heaven among the billowing clouds.

十四、简 狄

　　在很久很久以前,有两位美丽的少女,她们住在高高的九层楼台上,她们都是娇贵的女孩儿。每当吃饭的时候,都有音乐伴奏。

　　一天,天帝派了一只燕子去探望她们。燕子飞来,在楼台前呢呢喃喃叫个不停,姑娘们开心极了,便一起捕捉它。她们捕捉到后,用一只玉筐把它罩着,过一会儿,揭开玉筐去看,燕子飞走了,留下一只色彩斑斓的鸟蛋。姑娘们唱道:"燕子、燕子飞走了……"。后来姑娘们又去玩弄那个鸟蛋。姐姐简狄觉得好玩儿,便把鸟蛋衔在嘴里玩耍,但不知怎地,一下子鸟蛋滑到肚里去了。后来她便怀了孕,过了十四个月,生下了契,便是周民族的祖先。也有人说,简狄是去河里洗澡时,在河边捡到那颗鸟蛋,吃了以后,胸膛破裂而生的契。

14. Jian Di, a Girl Who Became Pregnant After Swallowing a Swallow's Egg

Long long ago there were two beautiful and indulged girls who lived high in the nine-storey house. Whenever they had dinner, musicians played for them. One day, a swallow, sent by the King of Heaven, chirped around the front of the house. The girls were so enchanted by it that they tried to catch it. After they caught it they covered it with a jade basket. Soon they uncovered the basket and the swallow flew away leaving behind a colorful bird's egg, so the girls sang songs such as "The Swallow has Flown Away".

They began to caress the egg. The elder sister, Jian Di, found the egg particularly fascinating. She put it into her mouth, but before she realized it, had swallowed it. After swallowing it, she became pregnant and fourteen months later, gave birth to Xie, the ancestor of the Zhou clan. According to other people, Jian Di took a bath in the river and picked the bird's egg from the riverside. After she ate the egg, her chest opened up, thus giving birth to Xie.

十五、姜嫄

　　从前有个名叫姜嫄的女子，据说也是帝喾的妃子。

　　一天姜嫄到野外去游玩，突然发现了一只脚印，那脚印是那样的大，比常人的大出了许多，她十分好奇地用自己的脚去踩。当她刚刚踩到拇指的地方，突然心里有所触动，回家后不久，便身怀有孕了。

　　后来姜嫄生了个胎衣包裹着的怪胎，像个肉球，她非常害怕，认为不祥。于是偷偷地把它扔到一条狭小的巷子里。这时，正好过来一群牛羊。巷子虽然狭窄，羊牛经过时却都小心翼翼，像是怕碰着它似的；姜嫄又把肉球捡起来，想把它抛到树林里去，可是当时正巧有许多伐木的人在砍树。于是只好又抱着它，想把它丢到水池里。水池已结了厚厚的冰，姜嫄有点于心不忍，但最后还是把它放到寒冷的冰面上。

　　这时，突然从天空飞来一只大鸟，它绕着肉球盘旋落下，将一只翅膀插在肉球下面，用另一只翅膀覆盖在上面去温暖它。

　　姜嫄感到惊奇万分，于是便向肉球走去。见有人来，大鸟便"嘎"地一声飞向高空。它边飞边叫，样子十分神秘。姜嫄俯下身去，只见胎衣裂开，并从中传出婴儿的啼哭声。那哭声又长又洪亮，传得很远很远；她赶忙抱起这个躺在冰面上的红彤彤的男孩，把他用衣服裹好带回家去了。她惊奇地想，这孩子一定不同凡响，说不定是个天上的神呢。因为姜嫄一度要把他抛弃，所以给他起名为弃。

　　据说这个弃，就是周民族的始祖。弃从小就喜欢农艺，他的民族也擅长农业。后来他的民族尊称他为后稷。

15. Jiang Yuan, a Girl Who Gave Birth to a Strange Looking Foetus

Once there was a girl, Jiang Yuan, who was said to have been the concubine of Di Ku. One day, while playing in an open field, Jiang Yuan suddenly happened upon an unusually large footprint, so feeling very curious, stepped on it. When she stepped on the big toe she felt something moving in her heart. Soon after she got home, she realized she was pregnant. Some time later, Jiang Yuan gave birth to a strange looking foetus wrapped up by afterbirth that looked like a fleshy ball. She became very frightened and thought it a bad sign, so she wanted to throw it away secretly in a narrow lane. At that time, a flock of sheep and a few oxen happened to be passing by. Even though the lane was very narrow, the sheep and oxen were very careful as if they were afraid to touch this strange package. So Jiang Yuan picked up the fleshy ball again and wanted to throw it into the woods. Yet there she found many loggers cutting down trees, so she had no choice but to carry it to a pond, hoping to throw it away there. However, a thick layer of ice covered the pond. At first Jiang Yuan took pity on the fleshy ball, but after some hesitation, she decided to put it on the cold ice.

Just then a big bird swooped down from the sky onto it. The bird put one of its wings under it and used the other wing to cover it. This surprised Jiang Yuan very much. When the large bird saw her walking towards the fleshy ball, it let out a cry and flew high up into the sky; still crying mysteriously it flew away. Jiang Yuan leaned down to find the afterbirth broken and from there came the cry of a baby. The loud, high-pitched cry could carry a great distance, so she hurriedly picked up this red boy who was lying on the ice. She wrapped him up with her clothes and carried him home. She thought the child must be very unusual or extraordinary and perhaps could even be a god. Because Jiang Yuan had once wanted to abandon him, she named him Qi, the Chinese for abandoned.

It is said that this Qi was the ancestor of the Zhou clan. And Qi, from a very young age, was interested in working the earth, so his clan became good at agriculture. His clan regarded him as Hou Ji, a god of grains.

十六、盘瓠

在很久很久以前，在中国这片土地上有一位被称做高辛的国王。

一天，他的王后得了一种奇怪的病，耳朵突然疼起来，那疼痛持续了三年。百般求医，无药可治。后来，不知从哪里来了一位老人，他从王后的耳朵里挑出了一只三寸长的小虫子，耳朵从此不疼了。王后感到又高兴又奇怪，就把那条小虫放在瓠里，又用一只盘子盖起来。

几天以后，那条小虫变成了一只小狗。小狗长着五色斑斓的皮毛。因为它是在盖着盘子的瓠中长大的，所以取名盘瓠。

盘瓠长得十分惹人喜爱，尤其是小公主简直与它形影不离。

那时高辛王的敌人——犬戎，经常侵犯边境，骚扰残害百姓，国王为此忧心忡忡，终日愁眉不展。一天，他宣令：如果有谁能杀死敌人的首领，并把他的人头带回来，就把美丽的公主许配给他。

从那以后，盘瓠就不见了，没有谁知道它的下落，连公主也不知它的去向。

盘瓠究竟到哪里去了？原来它正在无边无际的荒郊旷野中奔跑。几天之后，它来到了敌人的营地。敌人的首领看到这只可爱的小狗，非常高兴。他说："这不是高辛王的小狗盘瓠吗，这下子高辛王可要完蛋了，连他的狗都背弃了他，这真是个吉祥的兆头啊！"

于是，营地上举行了盛大的庆祝会，锣鼓彻夜响个不停。在宴会上，首领喝得酩酊大醉。他的护卫把他扶回帐篷，盘瓠寸步不离地尾随着他，夜深人静的时候，咬下了他的脑袋。

47

几天以后的一个早上，盘瓠叼着他的头发，把脑袋带回高辛王的宫中。盘瓠回来了，高辛王很高兴，尤其使他高兴的是他的仇敌的死亡。他下令把最好的肉拿来给狗吃。然而当肉放到盘瓠面前时，它连看都不看一眼就回到屋的角落里去了。三天三夜滴水不进。

国王明白了狗的心思，"啊，盘瓠，你为什么这样无精打采?"他说:"你是不是想要公主为妻? 我不想自食其言。可是人的女儿怎么能和狗结亲?"国王的话音一落，他就吃惊地听到狗说话了:"伟大的国王，我既然能由虫变成狗，当然也能由狗化为人。请您把我放到一座金钟下面，七天七夜不能看我，我就可以变成世上最英俊的男子。"

听了这话，国王高兴极了。于是便把它压在金钟下面。六天六夜过去了，什么事情也没有发生。到了第七天，公主开始坐立不安。"盘瓠已经这么些天不曾吃东西了，如果饿死可怎么办呢? 不如把金钟掀开一条小缝看看盘瓠是不是还活着。"她刚把金钟掀起，盘瓠就出来了。它变成了一个高大魁梧的青年，可是头部还没有来得及变。

公主哭得眼泪涟涟:"这全是我的过错，"她说，"即使盘瓠没有完全变成人，我也要嫁给它，我不能让我父亲两次失信。"

公主做了一顶狗皮帽子，嫁给了盘瓠。婚礼是在宫殿里举行的。之后盘瓠就带着公主到深山里去了。

一年又一年地过去了，谁也没有听到过有关公主的任何消息。王后非常担忧，便派遣士兵进山去寻找她。士兵们来到深山中，然而这里除了重云迷雾，却什么也看不见。他们越走，山越黑，脚下只有密树乱石。一连几次进山，都毫无结果。

最后国王决定亲自前往。国王临行那日，天气非常晴朗，在他眼前，呈现一座峻拔秀丽的大山，山上密林覆盖，山下有小溪深潭，遍地都是香气馥郁的白色小花。然而当国王和他的侍卫再往前走时，山里便腾起了云雾，前进的道路被落在地下的松枝阻塞。国王正要回转，他看到一些光着屁股的小孩儿在山石后尽情地玩耍。看到他，孩子们蜂拥而来，叫他爷爷。这时国王便明白了,这些孩子是神秘的盘瓠和自己女儿的儿女们。孩子们缠着他让他给他们取名,国王满足了他们的要求便返回了。

从此以后,这一带的山里就出现了一个民族,他们姓国王给取的姓氏,并把狗做为自己民族的祖先加以崇拜。

16. Pan Hu, the Dog Which Killed the King's Enemy and Married the Princess

Thousands of years ago, in the place which is now called China, lived a king whose name was Gao Xin. One day his queen got a terrible disease —there was a sharp pain in one of her ears. She suffered for three years, for nobody could cure her of it. One day an old man came and picked out a three-inch long golden worm from the queen's diseased ear. The pain stopped. The queen was very happy but she felt it very strange to see the golden worm, so she put it in a gourd bowl and covered it with a plate. Several days later, that worm changed into a dog with shining hair, the colours of the rainbow. It was named Pan Hu, which means gourd and plate in Chinese, because it was in the gourd covered with a plate that it changed into the form of a dog. Pan Hu grew very fast. All the people in the palace liked it, especially the princess who was always found with it.

At that time the king Gao Xin's enemy Quan Rong often launched attacks against his kingdom and killed his people. The king became very worried, so he declared whoever could kill the chief of his enemy and bring his head back should be the husband of the beautiful princess. After the declaration, Pan Hu disappeared, and nobody could tell his whereabouts, not even the princess.

The dog Pan Hu ran for days in the wilderness until he reached the camp of the king's enemy. The chief of the enemy became very excited on seeing the dog.

"Look!" he said. "Isn't that Gao Xin's famous dog Pan Hu? I am sure Gao Xin is doomed because even his dog has deserted him. Anyway, I'll take it as an auspicious sign from providence. "

So there was a great celebration in his camp with the beating of drums and gongs going on all night. At the banquet, he got very drunk. His soldiers carried him back to his own tent where the dog followed and bit him to death at night.

One morning several days later, the dog dragged the chief's head back by the hair. King Gao Xin was very glad to see the dog; he was even more glad to see his enemy's head. He ordered that Pan Hu should be given the best meat. However, the dog would not eat it when it was put in front of him. Pan Hu sadly went back to the corner of the room and stayed there for three days without any food. Then the king realized what the matter was and he went to the dog.

"Oh, my dear Pan Hu," the king said, "why are you so sad? Is it because you want to marry the princess? I hate to go back on my word, but you know, a human girl can't marry a dog. "

To his great surprise, he heard the dog speaking just like a human being:

"Oh, my great king!" it said, "since I can take the form of a dog, I can take the form of a humam being as well. Please put me under a golden bell for seven days and seven nights. Then you'll see the most handsome young man the whole world. "

The king was very glad to hear it and did as he was told. Six days and nights passed without anything happening. However, on the seventh day, the princess began to worry:

"Pan Hu hasn't had any food for such a long time," the kind princess said to herself. "What if he dies of hunger? I'll just lift the bell a little bit and see if he is still alive."

When the bell was lifted, Pan Hu came out of it. He had become a very tall and strong man but the head remained as before. It would have changed on the last day if the princess had not lifted the golden bell.

The princess cried and cried.

"It is my fault," said she. "I'll marry Pan Hu even if he can't change entirely into a human being, I won't make my father break faith with him once again."

The princess made herself a cap with dog's fur and married Pan Hu. The wedding took place in the palace. After the wedding, Pan Hu took the princess to a high mountain.

Several years passed without any news from the princess. The queen became very worried and bid the soldiers go to the mountain to look for her. The soldiers entered the mountain only to find it heavily covered with mist and clouds. The further they went, the darker the mountain became, all the paths, disappearing among the intricacies of wood and stone. The searchers were continually unsuccessful. Eventually, the king decided to go himself. The day when the king came, the weather was fine. He saw it was a beautiful mountain with dense forests, mountain streams, tarns and fragrant white flowers. However, when the king and his army went further, mists began to gather and they found their way blocked by interwoven branches of fallen pines. When the king was about to go back, to his

52

amazement, he spotted some naked babies playing behind the whitish rocks. On seeing him, the babies ran up to him, calling his grandpa. Then he realized they were children of the mysterious Pan Hu and his daughter — the princess. The babies asked him for names. The king named them. Then he kissed them and returned back. Later in the area around the mountain appeared a people who bear those names and worshipped the dog as their ancestor.

十七、廪　君

　　上古时候，在中国这片温暖的大地上，有着一座座大山，一片片荒野。那时通常是同一族的人居住在一个大山洞里。在南方的一座大山下有两个山洞，一个岩洞红似朱砂，一个岩洞黑得如漆。红洞里住的是巴氏族，黑洞中却住着樊氏、瞫氏、相氏、郑氏四个部族。两个洞的人经常互相打斗撕杀，死伤惨重。于是两个洞的老人们便聚在一起商议，如何避免伤亡。会上他们共同商定，举行一次比武会，由取得胜利的一方的首领做五族的共同首领，所有的人都要服从他的领导。红洞的人选举了务相做角斗的代表。比武的那天，各族所有的人都聚集在大山脚下。比赛的第一个项目是抛箭，每年参赛的代表都手握一柄短箭向对面的山洞中扔去。

　　比赛开始，五支箭同时飞越天空，结果只有务相的箭径直飞向山洞，其它的箭都在空中落了下来。第二个项目是乘泥船航行。五只泥船同时下水，船上各载一名参赛的代表。同样，其中的四只泥船很快地先后被河水冲垮了，只有务相所乘的船完好如初。他的船雕镂着美丽的图案，稳稳当当地在河中航行了很长的时间。毫无疑问，务相应该做所有氏族的首领。人们热烈而欢快地拥戴他，并称他为廪君，廪君就是部落首领的尊称。

　　廪君很爱他的臣民，大家过着和睦而富足的生活，因此人丁兴旺起来。这么一来，原来居住的山洞就不够住了，当地所采摘和猎取的果子和猎物也不够吃了。于是廪君就决定带领他的人民去别处开辟新的家园。他再一次登上了那条雕有花纹的神船，他的下民都乘坐着木船而开始了远航。

　　不久，他们来到了一个叫做盐阳的地方，潺潺的盐水在那里流淌，这里住着一位盐水女神。她明眸皓齿，不但美丽动人而且聪明异常。这位女神第一眼就看上了廪君，"请您在这儿留下吧！"她走来对廪君说："这是一块广阔的土地，您可以为您的百姓找到足够的盐和鱼，用不着再去找别的地方了。"廪君十分了解她的用意，她是为了能够得到他而挽留他的。实际上他也为这位美丽的女神而动心。但是他明白，这个地方并不像她所说的那么大，也没有足够的盐和鱼供他的百姓食用。作为一个部落的生活基地，这里太不理想了，所以他不能答应她。然而水神却迷恋着廪君，不忍与他离别。她想用炽热的爱情将他挽留住。夜晚她来与他幽会，清晨她便化做一只小虫与成千上万的同样的小虫一起组合成大块的黑云遮住阳光，使廪君和他的百姓难辨南北而无法前往。实际上，其它的小虫也是山神和水神变幻而来的。它们对于女神执着的爱情给予极大的同情，所以特来帮忙。廪君也了解她的所为，多次劝说她不要那样痴迷，并试图让她明白，过分的爱怜就意味着死亡。然而任性的水神却听不进去。

几个月过去了，廪君和他的人民在昏暗与混乱中生活着，眼看他们就会误掉打猎与摘果最好的季节。一天，廪君剪下了一撮长发派人送给女神，并对她说，他希望女神知道，长长的头发是永恒爱情的象征，因此希望她能系在自己的衣服下面。

早上，女神又一次变做飞虫，与其它的小虫一起在空中飞来飞去，廪君的头发也随着在空中飘荡。这时廪君拔出短剑向那只带着头发的飞虫掷去。随着一声惨叫，女神美丽的身躯从空中坠落，她面色惨白，双目紧闭。倾刻之间，所有的飞虫都烟消云散，于是人们又一次见到了蔚蓝色的清朗的天空和金色的太阳，处处传来了人们的欢笑声。只有廪君凝视着盐河湍急的流水，他的情人的尸体随着流水漂向远方。

迁徙的大军出发了，他们来到了盐水的尽头，那是一个黑黝黝的山谷，廪君非常失望。当他正要诅咒自己为什么这么不走运时，突然听到霹雳似的一声爆炸，之后，大家惊奇地看到，面前出现了一个阶梯，大家拾级而上，登上一片广阔而平坦的土地。那里有茂密的森林，蓝色的湖泊，潺潺的小溪，绿色的草坪,以及五颜六色的野花。廪君和他的人民惊喜万分,他们决定在这块土地上建立自己的家园。廪君每日和大家一起猎取禽兽,采集果实,然而当人们歇息的时候,廪君却独自忧伤地坐在一边,因为他在想念自己的情人——那红色的花瓣就像她的嘴唇,明澈的流水像她的眼睛,长长的轻柔的柳条像她的长发。他再也没有离开那个地方,因为那是盐水的尽头。廪君为了自己民族的存亡而杀死了自己的情人——盐水女神。

17. Lin Jun, a Tribal Chief Who Killed His Sweet Heart for His People

Once upon a time, China was very warm and there you could find wild animals which now only live in Africa. At that time, people of the same clan lived together in caves.

In the southern part of China there was a great mountain. At the foot of the mountain there were two caves, a red one and a black one. In the red cave lived a clan named Ba, in the black cave clans named Fan, Shen, Xiang, and Zheng. The people of the two caves often fought each other and many people died. In order to prevent more people from being killed in battle, the old people of the clans got together and had a discussion. At the meeting, they decided to hold a tournament. The champion would become the head of all five clans and everybody should obey him.

Wu Xiang, a very handsome young man was elected the representative of the red cave. On the day of the tournament, everybody went to the mountain. The first item was sword-throwing. Each competitor was holding a short sword, which was supposed to be thrown into the cave in the mountain yonder. As the contest began, five swords were thrown into the air, but all of them fell halfway except the one which belonged to Wu Xiang. Wu Xiang's sword flew all the way to the cave on the opposite mountain.

The second item was to sail in clay boats. Five clay boats were pushed into a river, each carryng a competitor. Again all the boats were washed away by the water except the one in which Wu Xiang was standing. That was a boat carved all over with beautiful patterns. It sailed for a long long time and remained the same as it had been. There was no doubt that Wu Xiang should become the chief of all the clans. The people accepted their leader warmly. He was called Lin Jun, which was the title for the tribal chief.

Lin Jun loved his subjects. The people of the clans lived a prosperous life and the population grew quickly. However, very soon the caves bacame too small for all of them, and the fruit and game also became inadequate. Lin Jun decided to take his people to look for a new place to dwell. He got on board the beautifully patterned magic clay boat, his people on ordinary wooden boats and they sailed along the river. Several days later they came to a place called Yan Yang where the Salt River (pronounced as Yan Shui in Chinese) lay in the centre.

The Goddess of the Salt River, who was of divine beauty and possessed of unusual wisdom, fell in love with Lin Jun at first sight.

"Please stay here," she came up to him and said, "This is a vast place and you can find enough salt and fish for your people. There is no need for you to go on with your exploring."

Lin Jun was fully aware of her intention — she wanted him for herself. Although he also loved the Goddess — for nobody could help loving such a beautiful woman —, he realized the place was not as large as she described, and it couldn't produce as much salt and fish for his people as she had asserted either. This place was far from being ideal for the tribe. No, he couldn't promise her.

58

The Goddess loved Lin Jun too much to part with him. So she tried to hold him with her ardent love. She came to him at night and in the morning she would take the form of an insect flying with a great many other insects which were actually gods and goddesses of rivers and mountains who had sympathy for her infatuation and had come to help. The insects formed large black clouds shielding the sunshine so that Lin Jun, who was ready to start with his people, couldn't tell the north from the south. This situation lasted for quite a long time.

Lin Jun knew it was the doing of the Goddess. Many a time he tried to persuade her to stop the folly and make her understand too much love meant death, but the wilful goddess would not listen. Lin Jun's people lived in confusion for several months and there was danger that they would miss the best season of the year for fruit and game. So one day Lin Jun cut some of his long hair and sent it to the goddess with the following message.

"The hair is long, so it is a symbol of everlasting love. Please wear it under your clothes so that you'll feel I am with you dead or alive."

The goddess failed to realize the real meaning of the message so she tied it to her underwear. In the morning, she became an insect again. Together with other insects she flew to and fro in the sky with Lin Jun's hair floating gracefully. Lin Jun took out his sword and threw it to the insect with the long hair. With a faint groan fell the beautiful body of the goddess from the sky, her face pale, her eyes closed. At the same time, all the other insects flew away. The sky cleared up: it was as blue as ever. The sun was shining and there was laughter everywhere. But Lin Jun was sad. He was staring at the hurried current of the Salt River which took away the body of his sweet heart.

On went the expeditionary army until they came to a place where the Salt River ended in a black valley. Lin Jun felt very disappointed. He was about to curse his bad luck when he heard a great explosion. To the amazement of all, a staircase appeared in front of them. They climbed the staircase and came to a vast space where they found hanging woods, blue lakes, rushing streams, green grass and colorful wild flowers. Lin Jun and his people were overjoyed to find such a nice place and they decided to make it their home. Lin Jun often went hunting and gathered fruit with his people, but when others were having a rest, he would go to some solitary place and sit there gloomily. For how could he forget his sweet heart when all around him were flowers as red as her lips, water as bright as her eyes and willow branches as long and graceful as her hair? He didn't go further than the Salt River, the Goddess of which he shot for the survival of his tribe.

第 二 章
帝 王 与 英 雄

CHAPTER TWO

KINGS AND HEROES

一、黄帝与四方天帝

　　黄帝的相貌长得很奇特,生有四张脸。他居住在天廷的中央,是中央大帝。土神后土手里拿着绳子辅佐他统管着四方。

　　东方的上帝是伏羲,他生有人的脸,蛇的身子。辅佐他的是木神句芒。句芒长的是人的脸,鸟的身子,方方的脸庞,穿着一件白色的衣裳,手里拿着一只圆规,骑着两条龙,掌管着春天。

　　南方的上帝是炎帝。火神祝融辅佐着他。祝融长着人的脸兽的身子,乘驾着两条龙,手里拿着一支称杆,掌管着夏天。

　　少昊是西方的上帝,他的儿子金神蓐收辅佐他。蓐收全身长着白色的毛,生有人的脸,老虎的爪子,左边的耳朵上挂着条蛇,乘驾着两条龙,手中拿着一把曲尺,掌管着秋天。

　　北方的上帝是颛项。水神玄冥,也就是禺强辅佐他。玄冥生着人的脸,鸟的身子,耳朵上挂着两条青蛇,脚下踏着两条青蛇,手中拿一个称锤,掌管着冬天。

1. Huang Di and the Gods of Four Directions

Huang Di, a most unusual looking god with four faces lived in the middle area of the celestial sky. The God of Land, Hou Tu, assisted him with a rope to take charge of all directions.

Fu Xi, the God of the East, had the face of a human being and the body of a snake. He was assisted by the God of the woods, Gou Mang, who had the square face of a human being and the body of a bird. In his hand, he held a compass. Dressed completely in white, he rode on two dragons. He was in charge of the spring.

The God of the South was Yan Di. The God of Fire, Zhu Rong, assisted him. Zhu Rong had the face of a human and the body of a beast. He rode on two dragons and held a scale in his hands. He was in charge of summer.

Shao Hao was the God of the West. His son Ru Shou, the God of Gold, assisted him. White hair covered Ru Shou's body. He had the face of a human, paws of a tiger and on his left ear hung a snake. He rode on two dragons and held a carpenter's square in his hand. He was in charge of autumn.

The God of the North was Zhuan Xu. The God of Water Xuan Ming, who was also called Yu Qiang, assisted him. Xuan Ming had the face of a human being and the body of a bird. On his ears hung two green snakes and under his feet were another two. In his hand, he held a steelyard. He was in charge of winter.

二、精卫填海

太阳神炎帝的小女儿,名叫女娃。一次她到东海去游玩,不幸被狂暴的海涛吞没,再也没能回还。女娃死后,变成了一只样子有些像乌鸦的鸟,头上的羽毛有着美丽的花纹,白色的嘴巴,红色的脚爪,名字叫精卫。住在长着很多柘桑树的发鸠山上。它鸣叫起来,那声音就像是在一声声地呼唤自己的名字。因为是大海无情地夺去了少女女娃的生命,所以,精卫常叼着西山的树枝和小石子,投到东海里去,一心要把大海填平。

精　　卫

2. Jing Wei, a Crow-like Bird Who Wanted to Fill Up the East Sea

The daughter of the God of the sun Yan Di was Nü Wa. One day while she was playing on the East Sea, she was unfortunately swallowed by the roaring sea and could never return home. After her death, she became a crow-like bird called Jing Wei. Crowned with decorative feathers, it had a white beak and red claws. And it lived on the mountain of Fa Jiu on which there were many cudrania tricuspidata. When it cried it seemed as if it were calling its own name. Because it was the sea that cruelly took Nü Wa's life away, Jing Wei often carried in its mouth the small branches and stones of the western hill, depositing them in the East Sea in the hopes of filling it up.

三、黄帝与炎帝的战争

　　很早以前，少典娶了有蛴氏的女子，生了黄帝和炎帝。黄帝在姬水之滨长大，炎帝在姜水之滨长大，所以，黄帝姓姬，炎帝姓姜。两个人品德不同，因此，他们之间常常发生战争。一次，因炎帝无道，黄帝发兵攻打炎帝，双方交兵在涿鹿的原野上。战斗十分激烈，死伤很多，致使血流成河，连旗杆都可在上面漂浮。情景甚是凄惨。最后，黄帝杀死了炎帝，占领了他的土地，天下才得以太平。

3. The War Between Huang Di and Yan Di

A long time ago, Shao Dian married a girl of You Jiao family who gave birth to Huang Di and Yan Di. Huang Di grew up by the banks of the Ji River whereas Yan Di grew up by the banks of the Jiang River, so Huang Di had the surname of Ji and Yan Di had that of Jiang. Because they were so different, they often warred with each ofther. Once as a result of something that Yan Di had done to anger Huang Di, Huang Di sent troops to attack Yan Di. The fight raged in the open country of Zhuo Lu and became so serious that many soldiers were killed or wounded. Their blood became a river on which even the flag pole could float. It was indeed a miserable sight. In the end Huang Di killed Yan Di and occupied his land. With that the world was peaceful again.

四、黄帝战蚩尤

蚩尤是炎帝的子孙后代。据说有八十一个或说七十二个弟兄。他们的形体相貌似人似兽,有的说是兽身人语,铜头铁额;有的更具体地描述说,他们长着人的身子,牛的蹄子,四只眼睛,六只手,牙齿有两寸长,而且坚硬无比,可以把沙子、石头当食物。

蚩尤想要和黄帝争夺天帝的宝座,发兵攻打黄帝。最初,黄帝还想用爱心来感化蚩尤,可是蚩尤不肯罢休。不得已,黄帝只得用战争来还击。

战争开始后,蚩尤的军队不仅强悍过人,蚩尤还能兴作遮天盖日的大雾,致使黄帝的军队在迷雾之中,辨不明方向,分不清敌我,接连打了好几个败仗。于是,黄帝便命令应龙来助战。在冀州的大平原上,应龙张开翅膀,呼云唤雨,向蚩尤还击。蚩尤立即请了风伯和雨师来对阵,一时间狂风四起,天昏地暗;大雨倾盆,漫天盖地,黄帝的军队站不稳,看不清,四散躲避。黄帝见此,只得又派了旱神魃来参战。魃秃头,身穿青衣。她一到,狂风骤雨消失了,顿时烈日炎炎,热浪滚滚。蚩尤的军队惊呆了。黄帝的军队趁势击杀了蚩尤,获取了胜利。

4. Huang Di Fought against Chi You

Chi You was the descendant of Yan Di. It was said that he had either seventy two or eighty one brothers who were simultaneously manlike and beastlike. Some people said they had the bodies of beasts but the language of humans. They had bronze heads and iron foreheads. Some described them in more detail. They said that they had human bodies with the hooves of oxen. They had four eyes, six hands and their teeth, at least two *cun* (about eight inches) long, were so hard that they chewed with ease sand and stones as their food.

Chi You wanted to fight against Huang Di for the crown of Heaven so he sent troops to attack him. At first Huang Di hoped to move him with his own kindness but all was in vain so he could do nothing but fight back.

The war started with Chi You's powerful troops in full force. Also, Chi You could stir up a dense fog completely obliterating both sky and sun. And so Huang Di's troops lost all sense of direction in the dense fog and couldn't distinguish the enemy from themselves. Therefore they were defeated several times. Seeing this, Huang Di ordered the dragon, Ying Long, to help them. On the Plain of Ji Zhou, Ying Long flapped his wings stirring up clouds and rain to fight against Chi You. And Chi You at once asked Feng Bo, the God of Wind, and Yu Shi, the God of Rain to fight with them, so there was a violent gale; the sky darkened and the rain poured down so the troops of Huang Di were unable to stand still or see clearly. All they could do was run for their lives. Seeing this Huang Di had to send Ba, the Goddess of Drought, to help them. Ba was completely bald and dressed in green. The moment she arrived the fierce gales and heavy rains disappeared. Only the scorching sun remained so Chi You's troops were shocked and Huang Di's troops were able to kill Chi You, winning finally.

五、猛志常在的刑天

在蚩尤之后，有一个被人们称作刑天的和黄帝争夺那上帝的宝座。刑天原是个无名的巨人，因为在战争中被黄帝砍掉了头，埋葬在常羊山，才被叫做"刑天"的。可是，他猛志常在，死犹不已，竟用自己的两个乳头当做眼睛用肚脐当做嘴，左手拿着盾牌，右手举着板斧挥舞不停，要继续争斗。

刑 天

5. Xing Tian, a Dead Giant Who Had a Fighting Spirit

After Chi You, the man, Xing Tian, wanted to fight Huang Di for the King of Heaven's crown. In the past Xing Tian had been an unknown giant and Huang Di, in a war, chopped off his head. He was buried on Mount Chang Yang so he was called "Xing Tian" or Punished-by-the-Gods. Even though he was dead, he still had a fighting spirit. His nipples became his eyes and his navel his mouth. He carried a shield in his left hand and an axe in his right hand. He waved these weapons continuously in the hopes of a fight.

六、追逐太阳的夸父

　　在北方大荒之中的成都载天山上，有一神人名叫夸父，他是炎帝的后代子孙。他的身材高大，力气超人，善走，手里握着两条黄蛇，耳朵上还挂着两条黄蛇。他想要追赶运行不止的太阳。

　　他一上路，就迈开双脚，如风似电地向西奔跑着，不知跑了多少路，一直追到禺谷，也就是太阳落下的地方。这时，红红的像个大火球似的太阳就在他的眼前，炽热的阳光烘烤着他。他感到烦燥口渴，想喝水，便去喝黄河、渭水的水。转眼间两条河水都被他喝干了，可他仍口渴难忍，不得不又向北奔去，想去饮大泽里的水。大泽在雁门山的北边，方圆有千里之广，是鸟雀繁衍小鸟和更换羽毛的地方。可惜他还没有到达大泽，就在中途渴死了。临死时，他弃掷了手中的杖，那杖落在地上，忽而化做一片枝叶茂密、硕果累累的桃树林。这片桃林，将会给后来寻求光明的人解渴消乏。

6. Kua Fu, the God Who Intended to Catch the Sun

On Mount Zai Tian in Chengdu in the north there lived the god, Kua Fu, a descendent of Yan Di. He was very large and of unusual strength. In his hand were two yellow snakes and on his ears there hung another two yellow snakes. A tremendous walker, he intended to catch the endlessly moving sun.

As soon as he set off, he swiftly ran toward the west, just like the wind and lightning. He ran a great distance until he came to Yu Gu, where the sun sets. At that time the sun, which looked like a massive fireball, was directly in front of him. The heat of the sun scorched him, upsetting him greatly and filling him with a great thirst. He went to drink the water of the Wei and Yellow Rivers. Drinking all the water of these two rivers in no time, he still felt extremely thirsty so he ran toward the north to drink the water of Da Ze, to the north of the Mount Yan Men. Da Ze covered the distance of a thousand *li*. It was the place where birds nested and shed their feathers. Unfortunately, before he got to Da Ze, he died of thirst, but before he died, he dropped his walking stick. The moment it fell on the ground it became a large peach grove with peach trees thick with leaves and full of peaches. And these peach trees would help people who went there to find light to quench their thirst and extinguish their fatigue.

七、为民除害的羿

据说在尧治理天下的时候,突然有十个太阳一齐出现在天空中。炽热、耀眼的阳光照射在大地上,就像是从天上撒向人间的火。土地被蒸烤得裂开了大缝;树木、花草、庄稼都枯焦而死;人们热得心烦意乱,透不过气来,而且眼看吃的东西也要断绝了。加之恶禽猛兽四出寻食,时时伤害着人和家畜,一场威胁着人们生存的灾难降临了。

尧带领着他的人民向天帝祈求、祷告。做天帝的帝俊知道后,立即派了一个善于射箭的天神名叫羿的到人间除害。羿的左臂生来比右臂长,对他挽弓射箭十分有利。临行前,帝俊特意赐给羿一张红色的弓,一袋白色的箭。红白相映,鲜丽异常。

羿领命带着他的妻子嫦娥降到人间,开始了他为人间解除灾难的工作。首要的便是除十日的工作。尧命令他用箭射掉那十个太阳。羿拉开红色的弓、搭上白色的箭,随着一只只射出的箭,一个个大火球似的太阳爆灭了,金色的羽毛在空中纷纷飘扬,太阳的精魂三脚乌鸦一只只地坠落在地上。羿一鼓作气,一连射下了九个太阳,只留下一个太阳在空中运行,用它的光和热为万物生灵造福。

羿胜利地完成了除十日的工作之后,便着手替人们消除为害的恶禽猛兽。

那时,中原大地上猰貐为害最厉害。猰貐,也叫"窫窳",原本是一位天神,长着蛇的身躯,人的脸。一次,被也是蛇身人脸的贰负神和他的一个臣子名叫危的合谋杀害了。后来,黄帝把他运到昆仑山,让巫师们用不死之药把他救活了。可是，活过来的猰貐却跳到昆仑山下的弱水里去，变成了一个奇形怪状吃人的猛兽。关于猰貐的长相，人们说法不一。有的说是龙头虎爪；有的说形似牛，红色的身子，人的脸，马的脚，叫唤起来，声音像是婴儿的啼哭声。

羿到了中原，凭借着神箭和高超的射技，没费吹灰之力，便灭掉了猰貐，为民除了又一害。

接着羿奉尧的命令来到南方的畴华之野，去诛杀一个叫做凿齿的怪物。凿齿具体长得什么样，今天已无从知道，但从有的说是人，有的说是兽来推测，大概是一个长着兽的脑袋，人的身子的怪兽。嘴里长着一颗长五六尺、样子像凿子的牙齿，十分锋利。凿齿用牙齿任意伤害善良的人们，一时没有人能制服他。

羿来到畴华之野，与凿齿对阵，手持红弓白箭，勇武过人，技艺超群。凿齿最初还拿了一把戈去还击，后来便只有手拿盾牌招架掩护，毫无还手之力了。最终，羿用神箭射杀了凿齿，再为民除一害。

羿从南方又折到北方的凶水，这里有一个长着九个头的怪物，名叫九婴。口中能喷水也能吐火，凶猛异常，对生活在这里的人们是一大祸害。羿和九婴经过一场激烈的战斗，天神羿把九婴射杀在黑浪滚滚的凶水之上，使这一方的人们免除了灾害，得以安居乐业。

羿射杀九婴之后，回过头来，经过东方的青丘之泽。人们告诉他，有一只很大很大名叫大风的鸷鸟，性情凶悍，力大善飞。每当它张开翅膀飞翔在空中时，就好像是一块云彩飘荡在空中，伴随他鼓动双翅，就会有巨风掠过大地，毁坏人们的房屋住所，人、畜都要受到伤害。

羿想这种力大善飞的鸟，不是一箭能致它死命的，他会带箭飞逃，养好伤，重新为害人们。因此，羿便用一条青丝绳系在箭尾，待鸷鸟飞得比较低的时候，一箭射去，正中大风的胸部。由于箭上系着绳子，大风没能飞逃，羿拉紧绳子，把鸷鸟拖下来，在地上杀死了他。东方的人们从此不再受大风之害。

羿刚刚射杀了大风，还没来得及喘口气，就又不得不赶到南方的洞庭湖去。因为洞庭湖里有一条叫巴蛇的大蟒，正在湖区为害。它掀翻渔船，吞食捕鱼的人们，致使这里的人们无法正常地从事渔业生产，生活不得安宁。

巴蛇体大无比，据说它能把一头大象囫囵地吞进肚子里去，三年之后，才把大象的骨头吐出来。有人还说，这被巴蛇吐出来的大象骨头，人若吃了能治心腹痛病呢。

面对这样的巨蟒，羿毫不畏惧，他驾着一叶小舟巡行在洞庭湖上，寻找那吃人的巴蛇。一天，湖上忽然白浪滔天，涛声如雷，在浪涛间一条大蛇正昂着头，嘴里吐出长长的像火焰一般的芯子，向着羿的小船游过来。羿判定这就是巴蛇。他从容不迫地拉弓搭箭向它射去，一连射中好几箭，巴蛇虽已受伤，淌着鲜血，可是还凶猛地向羿的船扑来。羿只得取出剑和巨蛇激战，巴蛇到底不是天神羿的对手，最终被羿斩做好几段，结束了它罪恶的生命。从此，鱼米之乡的洞庭湖区又恢复了往日的安宁。

最后，羿来到桑林，就是后来商汤遭遇七年大旱，带领人们向天帝祈雨的地方。这里有一种被人们叫做封豨（大野猪）的怪兽在作乱，它生着长长的嘴巴，巨大的犬牙从嘴里伸出来，身上长着稀疏的刚毛，力大如牛，十分凶恶。它不仅用长嘴巴掘食庄稼，也伤害人和家畜。一时间，人们被它搅得日夜不得安生。

羿一来到桑林，就用神箭射中了封豨，生擒了这个作恶的蠢家伙。

羿在人间，南征北战，东奔西走，一连为民除了七害，人们无不感念羿，颂扬他的神力和业绩，他在人们心目中是一位与日月同辉的英雄。

羿留在了人间，不知过了多久，他死去了。人们感念羿为民除害的恩德，尊奉他为诛邪除怪的宗布神。

7. Yi, the Archer Who Rid Humankind of Evil Monsters

It was said that when Yao took charge of the world, ten suns appeared in the sky. Scorching sunlight shone on the earth like flames from Heaven. The intense heat cracked the earth and woods. Flowers, grass and grain all died because of it. People were devastated, found difficulty breathing, and were about to run out of food. Wild beasts ran everywhere for food, often hurting people and livestock. And so a monumental disaster, threatening humanity's existence, dawned on mankind.

Yao took his people to pray to the King of Heaven. When Di Jun, the King of Heaven, heard this, he sent the god, Yi, a brilliant archer, to aid humans and eliminate the disaster. Yi was born with his left arm longer than his right so it was very easy for him to draw his arrows to shoot. Before he set out, Di Jun bestowed on Yi a red bow and a bag of white arrows, the strong contrast of the two colours creating great beauty.

Yi obeyed the order and came to the world of humans with his wife, Chang E, to eliminate the disaster. First of all, he was supposed to rid the world of the ten suns. Yao asked him to shoot them down, so Yi took out the red magic bow, put the white arrows in it and with arrows whistling, the flaming balls were shot down one after another. The golden feathers floated the sky and the spirits of the suns——three-footed ravens, fell to the ground one after another. Yi shot down nine suns at one sitting leaving only one sun in the sky to give its light and warmth to all living things.

After successfully shooting the suns, Yi started his task of eliminating the wild beasts. At that time, in the Central Plain, there was a fierce beast called Ya Yu. He used to be a god with the body of a snake and the face of a human being. At one time he had been killed by the God, Er Fu, who also had the body of a snake and the face of a human, and one of his subjects, Wei. Then Huang Di sent him to Mount Kunlun for the witches to revive him with an elixir. Yet the revived Ya Yu jumped into the Ruo River below Mount Kunlun and turned into a strange looking wild beast which could eat people. People had different stories regarding Ya Yu's appearance. Some said he had the head of a dragon and the paws of a tiger. Others said he looked like an ox. He had a red body, a face of a human and feet of a horse. When he cried, he sounded like a crying baby.

Yi arrived at the Central Plain with his innate skill and his magic arrows to assist him. He got rid of Ya Yu easily, doing humankind a great service by eliminating this wild beast.

After that Yi obeyed Yao's further orders and went to Chou Hua in the south to kill the monster, Zao Chi. People were not sure of Zao Chi's exact appearance, but some people said he was a human and some said he was a beast. From this we can conclude that he was probably a monster with the head of a beast and the body of a man. In his mouth was a chisel-like tooth about five or six *chi* (2 metres) long. People were unable to stop Zao Chi from hurting kind people with this sharp tooth.

Yi arrived at Chou Hua and fought with Zao Chi. He carried his red bow and white arrows. He fought very bravely and skillfully. At first Zao

81

Chi tried to fight back with a dagger but in the end, he could do nothing but defend himself with the shield. Finally, Yi killed Zao Chi with his magic bow and rid humankind of another beast.

From the south Yi went to the Xiong Shui River in the north where the nine-headed monster, Jiu Ying, lived. This fierce monster was a huge threat to the people in the area since it could spit out water as well as fire. After a bitter fight, the god, Yi, killed Jiu Ying in the torrential water of the Xiong Shui River so that people there could again live in peace.

After Yi killed Jiu Ying, he passed through Qing Qiu Lake in the east. People told him an enormous bird called Da Feng, or Great Wind, lived there. It was very fierce, very strong and good at flying. Whenever it opened its wings and flew, it seemed as if a large cloud floated through the sky. When it flapped its wings, it would create a tempest ruining people's houses and hurting their livestock.

Yi thought that since this bird was not only strong but good at flying, one arrow would only wound. It would still have the strength to fly away with the arrow in its flesh and once its wound healed, it would hurt people again. Therefore, Yi tied a rope on the arrow and when the bird flew relatively low, Yi shot it in the breast. Because the arrow was attached to a rope, Da Feng couldn't fly away. Yi pulled down the rope, pulling Da Feng to the ground with it, killing it there. From then on people in the east would never again suffer becaust of Da Feng.

As soon as Yi killed Da Feng, he had no time to take a breath; instead he went straight to Dongting Lake in the south. At that time there was a python called Ba She, or Snake, in Dongting Lake. It upset the fish boats and swallowed the fishermen so people there could no longer fish or live in peace.

This python was huge. It was said that he could swallow a whole elephant and not until three years later would it spit out the bones. People also said that if one ate the elephant bones spit out by the python, one could get rid of heart and abdominal pains.

Yi was not in the least afraid of facing this python. He rowed a boat along Dongting Lake looking for this people-eating python. One day suddenly some waves roared and pounded in the lake. In the waves, a large python held up his head and sticking out its flame-like tongue, swam towards Yi's boat. Yi thought it must be the python so he took out his bow and shot at it calmly, yet after he shot continuously at it, the python still fiercely leapt up towards his boat even though it was hurt and bleeding. Yi had to take out a sword to fight it. In the end, the python was no rival for the god, Yi, who cut it into several pieces, killing it. The area of Dongting Lake which was called the land of fish and rice, the area of abundance, resumed its usual peace.

Finally Yi arrived at Sang Lin, the place where Shang Tang came across a serious seven year drought, and took people to pray for rain. Here lived a monster called Feng Xi, a wild boar. It had a long snout, and its huge teeth extended from the snout. Its body was covered with thin tough hair. It had matchless strength. It not only ruined grain but also hurt people and livestock with its long snout. As a result, people could not live in peace at all.

As soon as Yi came to Sang Lin, he shot Feng Xi with his magic arrow and captured this villainous and foolish boar alive.

In the world of humankind, Yi went from north to south from east to west ridding the world of seven threatening monsters. People were very grateful to Yi for his magic power and heroic deeds, so in their hearts he was a hero as brilliant as the sun and the moon.

Yi remained in the world of humans and after many years, he died. To express their thanks to him, people worshipped him as the God of Zong Bu who could wipe out evils and monsters.

八、鲧禹治水

上古之时，一次发生水灾，洪水滔天，到处是汪洋一片。良田被淹，五谷不收，人们受着饥饿的煎熬；房屋被冲毁，无处安身，人们只好像禽兽一样以洞穴、树木为栖息之地，受着寒冷暑热的侵袭；凶禽猛兽还不时地伤害人们。大地之上渐渐人迹罕见，兽蹄鸟迹遍野。

于是，尧派大神鲧去治理洪水。鲧是黄帝的孙子，据说是黄帝生骆明，骆明生白马，白马就是鲧。鲧刚强耿直，办事果断。他十分同情人民的悲惨遭遇，可是单凭他自己的神力，又难以平息洪灾。他知道黄帝那里有名叫"息壤"的宝物，是一种生长不息的土壤。鲧便到天廷偷取了息壤，用来为人间解除灾难。

正在鲧专心致力治理洪水之时，不幸威严的黄帝知道了自己的宝物被窃的事，异常气恼，立即派祝融，就是那个长着兽的身子，人的脸，乘驾两条龙的火神，把鲧杀死在羽山的原野上。

大神鲧为人间治理洪水的愿望没能实现。他被杀后，精魂不灭，尸体竟然三年不腐烂。不仅如此，在他的肚子里还孕育着一个超过自己神力的大禹。

禹出世以后，果然不负父望，不仅具有极大的神力，且有决心完成鲧的未竟之业。天帝便赐息壤给禹，命他治理洪水。

禹治理洪水的方法比鲧高明，一方面让一只大黑乌龟驮着息壤随他而行，用息壤去堙障洪水；一方面令应龙在前面走，用尾巴画地，以疏导水流，使水流一直流向东方，注入大海。禹治理洪水，足迹遍天下，经历了千难万险,吃尽了苦头,最终取得了成功。使天下的人们脱离了灾难,过上了安居乐业的日子。

人们感激禹的功德,虞舜把帝位让给了大禹。禹做天子的时候,做了很多有益于人民的事。后来,他在一次巡视天下的时候,病死在南方的会稽,群臣就把他埋葬在那里。直到今天,会稽山还有一个洞穴,叫做禹穴,当地民间传说禹就是进了这个穴洞。

8. Gun and Da Yu, the Gods Who Controlled the Flood

In ancient times a massive, raging flood demolished fields and ruined grain, leaving people to starve. Houses floated away so people had nowhere to live. They were forced to live in caves or woods like wild animals where they suffered from the bitter cold of winter or the scorching heat of summer and the threat of wild animals. Gradually people became scarcer and scarcer. Human footprints were replaced by those of birds and beasts.

Thus, Yao sent the god Gun, Huang Di's grandson, to control the flood. It was said that Huang Di had a child called Luo Ming who in turn had a child, Bai Ma or Gun, Gun was strong willed and upright and always handled things decisively. He was very sympathetic with people's miserable fate but it was impossible for him alone to control the flood with his magic power. He knew that Huang Di had a treasure called Xi Rang, which was a kind of soil that could keep growing and in so doing could stop the flood. Gun went to the celestial court to steal Xi Rang and rid the world of its disaster.

When Gun was engaged in controlling the flood, the majestic Huang Di learned about the stealing of his treasure. Enraged he at once sent Zhu Rong, the God of Fire, who had the body of a beast, the face of a human and always rode on two dragons, to kill Gun in the open country of Mount Yu.

So the wish of the god, Gun, to control the water of the earth, was not fulfilled. After his death, his spirit lived; his dead body did not decay even after three years, and in his belly grew Da Yu who was to become even more powerful than he.

When Yu was born he lived up to the standard of his father. He was not only very powerful but was detemined to continue the unfulfilled wish of his father, Gun, so this time the King of Heaven bestowed Xi Rang on Yu and ordered him to control the flood.

Yu had better ways of controlling the flood than Gun. He asked a big black turtle to carry Xi Rang and follow him wherever he went so that he could use Xi Rang to prevent the flood. He also ordered Ying Long, the dragon, to walk in front of him and draw lines with his tail so as to dredge the water and make it flow to the east and finally into the sea. While he worked to control the flood, Yu travelled to many places encountering various dangers and difficulties but, in the end, succeeded. After that the people of the world were set free from the disaster and lived happily.

People were grateful to Da Yu for his successful work. Yu Shun gave his own crown to Da Yu. When Yu was king, he did many good and useful things for people. Later when he went on an inspection tour, he became ill and died in Kuai Ji in the south so his subjects buried him there. Even today you can find a cave called Yu Xue in Mount Kuai Ji. Local people say that Yu went into this very cave at that time.

第 三 章
奇 异 国 度

CHAPTER THREE

EXOTIC LANDS

一、大人国

　　来到中国神话世界,你可以漫游许多奇异的国家。在英国古典名著——《格列佛游记》中,有大人国、小人国,在中国古代神话中,也有个大人国。大人国地处东海波谷山。那里的人在母亲肚子里孕育三十六年才能出生,一生下来便是身材魁梧的巨人,而且头发是白的。他们没有学走路就会腾云驾雾。龙伯国与俍人国也是大人国,那儿的人高三十多丈,比十层楼还高。龙伯国的人能活到一万八千岁。据说原来他们的身材还要高,是天帝把他们缩小了。在古代神话中有个巨人,名叫防风氏,他被禹杀死,一部车子只能装下他的一节骨头。

1. Land of the Giants

　　Entering the world of Chinese myth, you can roam to many wonderful lands. In the famous classic British novel, *Gulliver's Travels*, there is the land of the giants, Brobdingnag, and the land of the little people or Liliput. In Chinese myth there is also the Land of the Giants situated in the East Sea on Bo Gu Mountain. Pregnancy lasted thirty-six years and upon birth, the "babies" were very strong and tall giants. Their hair was completely white, and even before they could walk, they could mount the clouds and ride the mist. The country of Long Bo and that of Tiao Ren were both the Land of Giants. People there were thirty *zhang* (100 metres) tall, even taller than a ten storey building. People in Long Bo could live up to eighteen thousand years. It is said that at one time they had been even taller; however, the King of Heaven made them shorter. According to ancient myth, a giant called Fang Feng was killed by Yu, and the cart could only hold one of his bones.

二、小人国

在中国古代神话中,同样有小人国。小人国的国名叫焦侥国。那里最高的人也只有三尺,一般的人只有一尺五寸高。他们居住在山洞里。平日耕地务农,还能制造各种灵巧的东西。在西方海外,还有另一个被称做鹄国的小人国,国民身高只有七寸左右,然而他们却都彬彬有礼,见人就行礼,寿命能活到三百多岁,他们善长行走,一天能走一千里地。

2. Land of the Dwarfs

In ancient Chinese myth there is also a land of the tiny dwarfs called Jiao Yao. The tallest people there were only three *chi* (one metre) and the ordinary ones stood only one and a half *chi* (about one third of a metre) tall. They lived in mountain caves and plowed the fields and farmed. They could also make all sorts of delicate things. Beyond the sea in the west there was another land of even smaller dwarfs called Hu and people there were only about seven *cun* (70 centimetres) tall, even shorter yet. They were all very polite and bowed whenever they saw anyone. They could live up to three hundred years. Excellent walkers, they could walk 1,000 *li* (500 kilometres) per day.

三、交胫国

　　东方有个交胫国,这个国度的人个子都很矮,只有四尺左右,身上长毛,他们的腿脚没有骨节,而且弯曲,互相交叉着,所以一旦倒地,自己就爬不起来,须要别人搀扶才能重新站立起来。

3. The People of Jiao Jing

　　In the east was a country called Jiao Jing. People there were extremely short, only about four *chi* (1.33 metres) tall. Their bodies were covered with hair and their legs and feet had no joints. Their legs were intertwined so whenever they fell down they could not get up by themselves. They had to be helped up by others.

四、君子国

在九夷一带有个君子国，那个国度的人，衣着整齐，身佩宝剑，每人身后都有两头老虎做他们的仆人，不过那虎比猫还要服从听话，从不伤人。君子国的人都懂得谦让，因此国内从无战乱，臣民的寿命也很长。

4. Jun Zi: the Country of Gentlemen

In the area of Jiu Yi there was a country of gentlemen, where people dressed very fastidiously and all carried a sword. Two tigers, even more gentle and obedient than cats, stood behind each person ready to serve. The people here never hurt anyone and they were all very polite so there were never any wars and the people lived to a ripe old age.

五、轩辕国

古代神话中，还有个轩辕国。据说轩辕国的臣民是黄帝的子孙。他们长着人的脸，蛇的身子，尾巴缠在头上。那国的人最少能活到八百岁。这个国家的附近，有座轩辕台，四条蛇盘绕其上守卫着，射箭的人都不敢向这里发箭，所以人们平安地生活着。

轩辕国

5. The Country of Xuan Yuan

In Chinese myth there is a country called Xuan Yuan and it is said that people in this country were descendants of Huang Di. They had the face of humans and the bodies of snakes with their tails wound around their heads. People there could live at least eight hundred years. Nearby this country was a platform called Xuan Yuan and four snakes were entwined around it to keep guard. Archers dared not shoot at this place so people lived peacefully.

六、无臀国

在西方,有个无臀国,有的书上做"无继"国,意思是说这个国度的人没有男女之分,所以没有后嗣。既然没有后代,怎么会长期生存呢?原来在他们死后,心脏仍在跳动,埋在土里过一百二十年,就又复生为人了。他们住在洞穴里靠喝空气、吃鱼来维持生命。

6. The Country of Wu Qi

In the west was a country called Wu Qi. Some books said it was called Wu Ji, indicating that there was no difference between men and women and there were no descendants. If there were no differences between men and women and they had no descendants, how could the country develop and exist for such a long time? After their deaths, their hearts still beat and after they had been buried in the earth for one hundred and twenty years they revived. They lived in caves and depended on air and fish to live.

七、枭阳国

枭阳国，又叫赣巨国，地处北方。那里的人身长一丈左右，面部长相像人，浑身长满黑毛，胳膊很长，脚是反方向生的，然而走起路来，十分迅疾。他们的嘴唇特别大，笑起来嘴唇上翻，可以遮盖住脸面。他们见了人就笑，笑够了就把人吃掉。

7. The Country of Xiao Yang

The country of Xiao Yang was also called the country of Gan Ju which lies to the north. People there were one *zhang* (3. 3 metres) tall. Their faces looked human and they were covered with black hair. They had extremely long arms and although their feet grew in the reverse direction, when they walked, they were very swift. Their mouths were very large and when they laughed their mouths could turn up to cover their face. They would laugh whenever they saw people and they would eat them when they stopped laughing.

八、奇肱国

西方有个奇肱国,也叫奇股国,地处离玉门关四万里的地方。据说这里的人只长着一只胳膊,却有三只眼睛。常常乘坐一种叫"吉良"的花斑马,这马长着红色的鬃毛,眼睛像黄金那么明亮。在它的周围还有两只鸟,有两个头,羽毛红中带黄。奇肱国的人心灵手巧,善于制造机械,用来捕获鸟兽。他们制造的一种飞车,还能随风远行呢。

奇肱国

8. The Country of Ji Gong

In the west was a country called Ji Gong, also called Ji Gu. It was forty thousand *li* (twenty thousand kilometres) away from Yu Men Guan,

99

a very remote place. It is said that people there had only one arm and three eyes. They often rode piebald and red-maned horses called Ji Liang who had eyes as bright as gold. Each horse was surrounded by two red and yellow feathered birds with two heads. People in the country of Ji Gong were clever and deft. They were good at making machinery to catch birds and beasts. A kind of flying cart made by them could also soar a long way with the wind.

九、三首国

在南方的海外,有个三首国,这里的人身上都长着三个脑袋,模样十分怪异。

9. The Country of the Three Heads

Beyond the sea in the south was the country of the Three-Heads, so called because its strange looking population all had three heads.

十、雨师妾国

在南方海外有个雨师妾国，这里的人全身都是黑色皮肤，两只手中各握一条蛇，有时也各握一只乌龟；他们左耳朵上挂着一条青蛇，右耳朵上挂着一条红蛇。

雨师妾

10. The Country of Yu Shi Qie

Beyond the sea in the south was a country called Yu Shi Qie. People there were very dark and held a snake in each hand. Sometimes they held a turtle instead. A green snake dangled from each person's left ear and from each person's right ear dangled a red snake.

102

十一、跂踵国

　　东北方有个跂踵国，这国的人身材很高，两只脚更大得出奇。他们走起路来单用五个脚趾，而足跟是不着地的。

11. The Country of Qi Zhong

In the northeast there was a country called Qi Zhong and people there were very tall with extremely large feet. They always walked on their toes.

十二、博父国

北方海外有个博父国,据说他们是当年追逐太阳的夸父的后代,他们身材高大,右手握一条青蛇,左手握一条黄蛇。在他们住地的东边有两株枝叶茂密的桃树,这是当年夸父逐日,道渴而死前所丢弃的拐杖变成的,虽然只有两棵树,却覆盖了大片的土地。

12. The Country of Bo Fu

Beyond the sea in the north was the country of Bo Fu. It is said that the people there were descendants of Kua Fu, the one who ran after the sun. They were very tall and each held a green snake in his right hand and a yellow snake in his left. To the east of their residences were two dense peach trees. The stick left by Kua Fu before he died of thirst turned into these two peach trees. Although there were only two trees, they covered a large area of land.

十三、聂耳国

聂耳国在北方海外，这个国家的人身上有老
虎斑纹，都长着一对特大的耳朵，耳朵一直能垂到
腰部。走路的时候必须用两手托着。据说他们睡
觉的时候，常常用一只耳朵做垫席，一只耳朵当被
子盖。平时使唤着两只花斑虎。

13. The Country of Nie Er

The country of Nie Er lay beyond the sea in
the north. People in this country had figurative
designs of tigers on their bodies and they all had
extremely large ears which hung to their waists,

聂耳国

so when they walked they had to support their ears with their hands. It is
said that when they slept they often used one of their ears for their mattress and the other for their quilt. They used two tigers as their servants.

十四、一目国

　　北方有个国家叫一目国。这里的人长着人的面孔，却只有一只眼睛，眼睛长在脸的中央。因为人长得很怪，所以人们把这个国度称为鬼国。鬼国中妖物鬼怪处处可见。例如有一种野兽叫陶犬，它长得像狗，毛色是青的，吃人时从头部开始；还有一种叫穷奇的怪兽，形状像老虎，却长着翅膀，也吃人。这里的昆虫，个头也特别大，而且很奇特。有一种黑色的蜂，长得像蝗虫，个头有茶壶那样大。还有一种长着人脸，野兽身躯，浑身青色的妖物。

14. The Country of Yi Mu，
the One-Eyed People

In the north was the country of the One-Eyed People，which was called Yi Mu. People there had human faces but had only one eye in the centre of their faces. Because people looked very strange，it was called the country of ghosts. In the country of the ghosts one could see devils and ghosts everywhere. For instance there was a wild beast called Tao Quan. It looked like a dog with green fur. When it ate people，it started from the head. There was another kind of strange beast called Qiong Qi which looked like a winged tiger. It also ate people. Insects in this country were

106

also very large and unusual. A kind of black wasp looked like a locust and had the size of a large teapot. And there was also a green monster which had the face of a human and the body of a wild beast.

十五、长 股 国

　　过去有一个长股国，国民皮肤都是黑的，披着头发，脚有三丈长，所以又叫长脚国。据说长脚人常常背着住在它西边的长臂人到海中捕鱼，而长臂人呢，身材和普通人差不多，可是胳膊却有三丈长。长股国的员丘山上长有长生不死的树，他们采集了树的果实，吃了可以长生；山下有个赤泉，他们喝了泉里流出的水，可以不老。所以这个国度的人们是长生不死的。

15. The Country of Chang Gu

In the past there was a country called Chang Gu where all the people were dark skinned with disheveled hair. Their feet were about ten metres long so the country was also called the country of the Long-Feet. It is said that people in the country of Long-Feet often carried the long-armed people who lived to the west to the sea in order that they might catch fish. The people with long arms were similar to ordinary people but their arms were about three *zhang*（about ten metres）long. And on Mount Yuan Qiu，also in the country of Chang Gu，was a tree of immortality. People collected the fruits of this tree so that they could live forever. Under the foot of the mountain was a red spring，and if people drank its water，they also became immortal.

十六、一臂国

一臂国的人，不用说当然国人只长着一只胳膊，而且也只一只眼睛和一个鼻孔。连这个国家中生活着的一种浑身虎纹的黄马，也只长着一只眼睛和一只前腿。

16. The Country of Yi Bi,
the One-Armed People

The population in the country of the One-Armed People each had one arm, one eye and one nostril. In this country lived a type of yellow horse covered in tiger-like designs. Even this horse had only one eye and one foreleg.

十七、三身国

在西方大荒之中,有个三身国。三身国的人一个脑袋三个身子,据说是帝俊的妻子娥皇的子孙后代,吃食主要是黍子。这里靠不庭山,山下有四个深潭,其中南面的那个叫从渊,据说是舜帝洗澡的地方。

17. The Country of San Shen, the Triple Bodies

In the open country of the west was a place called Triple Bodies. People there, who were said to be the descendants of E Huang, the wife of Di Jun, had only one head and three bodies. Their main food was millet. The country was near Mount Bu Ting. At the foot of the mountain were four deep ponds. The one in the south was called Cong Yuan and it was said to be the place for Shun Di to take a bath.

十八、羽民国

在西南地区有个羽民国，他们的脸颊很长，头发是白的，红眼睛，长着鸟一样的嘴巴。人人都生一双翅膀，能飞，但飞不很远。据说他们和鸟类一样，是卵生。国内生长着很多凤凰一类的鸟，羽民国的人吃鸟蛋。国中还生长着一种野兽，形状像豹，但毛色是绿的。

羽 民 国

18. The Country of Yu Min

In the area of the southwest, there was a country called Yu Min. The people of this country had very long cheeks, white hair, and red eyes. They had birds' beaks and wings so they could fly short distances. It is said that they were oviparous, just like birds. In this land were many birds like the phoenix and people in this country ate bird eggs. There was also a wild beast which looked like a leopard, but with green fur.

十九、讙头国

讙头国,也称做讙朱国。这个国家的人,长着人的面孔,却长着鸟一样的尖嘴。背上生一对翅膀,却飞不起来,走起路来手扶翅膀,足翅并用,他们靠捕食海中鱼虾生活。

讙头国

19. The Country of Huan Tou

A country called Huan Tou was also called the country of Huan Zhu. People in this country had pointed mouths, the faces of humans, but bird beaks. On their backs were wings but they could not fly. When they walked they had to support their wings with their hands and use their feet and wings at the same time. They relied on catching fish and shrimps in the sea.

二十、厌火国

南方海外有厌火国，这个国家的人长得很像猕猴，但皮肤是黑的。据说他们拿火炭作食品，所以人人嘴里都能喷出火焰。国内有一种野兽，名叫祸斗，长得很像狗，专吃狗排出的粪便，很凶恶，经常喷火伤人。

厌火国

20. The Country of Yan Huo

Beyond the sea in the south was the country of Yan Huo. People in this country all looked like macaques but their skin was black. It is said that they used charcoal as their food so that everybody could spit flames. In this country there was a kind of wild beast called Huo Dou. It looked very much like a dog and relied on dog's excrement for sustenance. It was very fierce, often spurting flames to hurt people.

二十一、裸　国

南方有个裸国，一年四季全身都赤身露体、在他们的胸前刺有美丽的花纹，两只眼睛下面，也画着粉色、紫色图案，他们往往拔去前面两个牙齿，做为一种美饰。凡进入这个国度的人，都要脱去上衣。据说大禹治水经过裸国时，也脱去上衣，尊重了他们的风俗习惯。

21. The Country of Nakedness

In the south was a country of nakedness where people remained nude throughout all four seasons. On their chests were beautiful designs and they drew pink and purple patterns under their two eyes. They generally pulled out their two front teeth as a kind of ornamentation. Whoever wanted to enter this country was required to take off their upper clothes. It is said that when Da Yu passed through this country while he was controlling the flood, he also took off his upper garments to show his respect for their customs.

二十二、贯胸国

南方海外有个贯胸国,又叫穿胸国。这个国家的人胸前有个圆洞直通后背。他们怎么会成这副样子呢? 据说大禹平天下后,大会群神,当时防风氏首领迟到了,禹把他杀死。后来禹到海外各国巡视,路过防风氏部族,防风氏部族的两个臣子为报禹杀君之仇,就弯弓搭箭向禹射去。这时风雨大作,有两条龙载着禹腾空而去。这两个臣子自知闯了大祸,拔出刀穿胸自杀。后来禹知道了这件事,感叹这两个臣子的忠心,叫人替他们拔出短刀,敷上不死之药。于是这两个人又复活了,而胸前却留了个大洞。说来也很有意思,这国的头领外出时,只要把上衣脱去,让手下人用竹竿或木棍当胸一穿抬着就走了。

22. The Country of Guan Xiong

Beyond the sea in the south was a country called Guan Xiong or Chuan Xiong, meaning "going through the chest". People in this country all had a hole in their chest which went right through their back. How could this have happened?

It is said after Da Yu took charge of the entire world, he gathered all kinds of gods and the head of Fang Feng clan was late so Yu killed him. Later when Yu went on an inspection tour in different countries, and when he passed by the clan of Fang Feng, two subjects from that clan took out their bows and arrows to shoot at Yu in revenge. Suddenly wind and rain appeared and two dragons flew away carrying Yu. These two subjects knew they were in deep trouble so they took out knives and killed themselves by cutting through their chests. Later, when Yu learned of this, he sighed; moved by the loyalty of these two subjects. He asked someone to pull out the knives and pour some elixir on their chests. Thus these two people were revived, yet there remained a big hole in their chests.

The interesting thing is that whenever the head of the country wanted to go out, he would just take off his upper garments and his subjects would put a bamboo of pole or stick through his chest to carry him.

二十三、钉灵国

钉灵国在北海之内,这个国家的人,膝部以上长得同常人一样,但膝部以下,小腿生毛如马的小腿,下生马蹄,因此他们不骑马而跑起来比快马还要迅疾。

23. The Country of Ding Ling

The country of Ding Ling was in the North Sea. People in this country were just like ordinary people above the knee but below the knee they had hairy calves just like those of horses and they had hooves, so they could run even faster than the best of horses.

二十四、日林国

　　古代神话中有个日林国，生产数千种神药。日林国的西南方有一面巨大的石镜，方数百里，晶莹透亮，可以照出人的五脏六腑，所以人们称它是仙人镜。国中的人如果生了病，到镜前一照，便可以知道是哪个部位有病灶，然后采集神药，对症治疗，没有治不好的。所以日林国的人都很长寿，能活到三千岁。

24. The Country of Ri Lin

In ancient mythology, there was a country called Ri Lin, where grew several thousand kinds of magic medicine. In the southwest of the country was a giant stone mirror which covered an area of several hundred *li*. It was as bright as crystal so it could reflect people's vital organs. Thus it was called the immortal mirror. If it happened that people in the country fell ill, they would go and look in the mirror and then they would know what was wrong with them. Unfailingly, they could collect magic medicine to cure themselves. As a result, people in the country of Ri Lin all lived long, up to three thousand years.

第四章
异　　物

CHAPTER FOUR

STRANGE CREATURES

一、奇异的动物

鹿蜀

在杻阳之山，有一种名叫鹿蜀的兽，长得很像马，白色的头，赤红色的尾巴，身上长着老虎似的花纹，它鸣叫时的声音就跟人的歌声一样。

九尾狐

青丘之山上，有一种九尾狐，它的叫声如同婴儿声音，能吃人。据说人吃了九尾狐的肉，能辟妖邪之气。

獿如

一种名字叫獿如的动物，样子很像鹿，头上长着四只角，有一条白色的尾巴，四只脚长得不一样，后边两脚和马蹄一样，前边两脚长得像人的手。

獿如

狍鸮

狍鸮

钩吾之山有一种食人的兽，叫狍鸮。她长着羊的身子，人的脸，眼睛不长在脸上，而长在腋下，生着和老虎一样的牙齿，人的手，叫唤起来声音像婴儿。

天　马　　　　　　　　　　　凤皇

天马

有一种兽，名叫天马，见了人就飞，它身子像是一只白色的狗，而头是黑色的。鸣叫起来如同大声呼叫自己的名字一样。

蛮蛭

在凫丽之山，有一种食人的兽，样子极像狐狸，名叫蛮蛭，长着九个头，九条尾巴，虎爪，叫唤的声音像婴儿一样。

凤皇

凤皇鸟生活在丹穴之山上，长得虽然很像鸡，可身上的羽毛有五彩花纹。头上的花纹曰德，翅上的花纹曰义，背上的花纹曰礼，胸上的花纹曰仁，肚子上的花纹曰信。这种鸟饮食自然，自歌自舞。它一出现，天下则和平安宁。

猙池

在基山上,有一种长得像羊,名叫猙池的兽,它长着九条尾巴,四个耳朵,眼睛生在脊背上。在这里还有一种和鸡很相像的鸟,名字叫鹏鶘,长着三个头,六只眼睛,六只脚,三个翅膀。据说人吃了它的肉,精神百倍不犯困。

橐𣬠

羭次之山的橐𣬠鸟,生着人的脸,只有一只脚。冬天出来,夏天蛰伏。据说人佩戴它的羽毛,不怕天上的雷击。

猙池　　　　　　　　　橐𣬠

鹠鸟

翠山上的鹠鸟,长得像鹊,羽毛呈赤黑色,长着两个头,四只脚。

鹠鸟　　　　　　　　　文鳐鱼

123

文鳐鱼

文鳐鱼长得像鲤鱼，可是，在鱼的身子上长着鸟的翅膀，青苍色的花纹，白色的头上长着红色的嘴。常从西海游到东海，夜间能飞行。它鸣叫的声音和鸾鸡声相似。它的肉味酸甜可食，据说吃了文鳐鱼可以治好狂病。而且它一出现，天下就会有一个五谷丰收的好年成。

儵鱼

古代神话中说有一种儵鱼，长得和鹊一样，但羽毛呈赤红色，有三个尾巴，六只脚，鸣叫的声音也像鹊，吃了它的肉可以无忧无虑。

何罗鱼

神话中还说在谯水中有很多何罗鱼，这种鱼长着一个头，却有十个身子，它叫唤的声音和狗吠一样。人吃何罗鱼能治好痈疮。

人鱼

一种人鱼，有四只脚，声音像婴儿。吃了人鱼肉使人不得痴呆症。

鳛鱼

鳛鱼是一种奇异的鱼，长得和鱼一样，却生有鸟的翅膀，出入有光随行，声音和鸳鸯相似。它一出现，天下便会有大旱灾。

三足龟

在某座山的南面狂水中，生长着很多三只脚的龟，人吃了三足龟的肉，不生大病，还能医治好肿痛。

1. Rare Animals

Lu Shu

On Mount Niu Yang lived a kind of beast called Lu Shu. It looked very much like a horse except it had a white head, a crimson tail, and some tiger-like designs on its body. And its cry was just like a person singing.

Nine-tailed Fox

On Mount Qing Qiu was a kind of nine-tailed fox. Its cry was also just like a baby's and it ate people. It is said whoever ate the meat of this nine-tailed fox could get rid of any evil.

Ying Ru

An animal called Ying Ru looked very much like a deer. It had four horns on its head and a white tail. Its four feet were not the same; the hind feet were like a horse's hooves and the forefeet were like a human's hands.

Pao Xiao

On Mount Gou Wu lived a man-eating beast called Pao Xiao. It had the body of a sheep and the face of a human. Its eyes were not on its face but under its armpits. It had teeth like a tiger, hands like a human, and when it cried it too sounded just like a baby.

Tian Ma

A beast called Tian Ma flew away whenever it saw people. Its body looked like a white dog, but its head was black. When it cried, it seemed as if it were calling its own name.

Long Zhi

On Mount Fu Li lived another man-eating beast. It looked very much like a fox and was called Long Zhi. It had nine heads, nine tails and tiger paws. And its cry was just like that of a baby.

Feng Huang

A Feng Huang bird lived on Mount Dan Xue. Although it looked like a rooster, the feathers on its body had colorful designs. The designs on its head represented virtue, the figures on its wings represented justice, the feathers on its back represented courtesy, the figures on its chest represented benevolence, and the designs on its belly represented faith. This bird lived on natural things and often sang and danced. Its appearance signified peace.

Bo Yi

On Mount Ji lived a beast called Bo Yi which looked very much like a sheep. It had nine tails, four ears, and its eyes were on its back. On this mountain also lived a bird that looked very much like a rooster called Bie Fu. It had three heads, six eyes, six feet and three wings. It is said that

126

those who ate its meat would be in high spirits and forever energetic.

Tuo Fei

The Tuo Fei bird on Mount Yu Ci had the face of a human but just had one foot. It came out in winter but hibernated in the summer. It is said that people who wore its feathers would not be struck by lightening.

Lei Bird

The Lei bird on Mount Cui looked like a magpie. Its feathers were pitch black and it had two heads and four feet.

Wen Yao Fish

The Wen Yao fish looked like a carp yet on its body were the wings of a bird and green designs. It had a white head and a red mouth, and it often swam from the West Sea to the East Sea—even flying at night. Its cry was just like that of a mythical bird like the phoenix. Its meat tasted both sweet and sour. People said that if you ate the Wen Yao fish it could cure madness. Also, whenever it appeared harvests would be good throughout the world.

Shu Fish

According to ancient myth, there was a particular fish called Shu which looked like a magpie but its feathers were crimson. It had three tails, six feet and its cry was just like that of a magpie. Eating its meat would make one carefree.

He Luo Fish

Ancient myths tell of many fish called He Luo who inhabited Qiao River. This fish had one head but ten bodies. Its cry was just like that of a barking dog. Eating the flesh of He Luo could cure skin ulcers.

Man-Fish

A man-fish had four feet and its cry was just like a baby. Eating its meat could prevent insanity or dementia.

Hua Fish

The Hua fish was very unusual. It looked like a fish but had bird wings and a light that appeared with it wherever it went. Its cry was just like a mandarin duck. Whenever it appeared there would be drought throughout the world.

Three-footed Turtle

In the roaring water to the south of a mountain lived many three-footed turtles. Those who ate the meat of a three-footed turtle would not fall seriously ill and this magical creature could also cure painful swelling.

二、奇草异木

祝馀

在招摇山上，生长着一种名叫祝馀的草，它很像韭菜而开青色的花。人们吃了肚子就再也不饿了。

蓝荔

小华山上，有一种草叫蓝荔，它长在石头上，也缘木而长。吃了它可以治好心痛病。

多条草

符禺山上长着一种多条的草，开着红花，黄色的果实，形状很像婴儿的舌头。吃了它能使人头脑清醒消除困惑。

黄雚草

竹山上的黄雚草，形状像臭椿，叶像大麻，开白花，结出黑色果实，用它浸泡水洗澡，可以治好疥疮。

熏草

浮山上有一种草，名叫熏草，叶子像大麻，而茎却是方形的，开白花，果实呈黑色。

鬼草

牛首山上的一种草叫鬼草,茎呈红颜色,也像稻、粟一样吐穗结实,吃了它,可以解除人们心中的烦忧。

无条

苦山上长一种叫做无条的草,圆叶无茎,服用它可以预防甲状腺肿大。

杜衡草

天帝山上生长着一种杜衡草,可以用来治愈口颊坏疽和甲状腺肿大。

无名树

仑者山上生长着一种像谷子的树,树的纹理呈红色,它能分泌出一种黑漆似的汁液,味道像麦芽糖。吃了它不但顶饥,还可以解除疲劳,也能用它来染玉。

櫰木

中曲山有种树,名叫櫰木,叶子是圆的,红色的果实大如木瓜。吃了它可以增大力气。

文茎

符禺山上的一种树,名叫文茎,果实像枣,能治耳聋。

无名树

北号山,面临北海。山上有一种树,长得像杨树,开红花,结的果实像枣,但没有核,味道酸甜。吃了它可以不得疟疾。

芑树

东始山有一种树,名叫芑树,红色纹理,能分泌出一种红色的汁液,用这种树汁涂马,马就变得易于驯服了。

黄棘

苦山上的黄棘树,长着圆叶,开黄花,果实像兰,妇女们如果误吃了它,就不能生育了。

帝休

少室山上,百草树木环山而生。其中有一种树,名叫帝休,叶子像杨树叶,树枝交错相重五出,开黄花,结出黑色果实,吃了它可以制怒。

桃树

东方有一种桃树,高五十丈,叶长八尺,果实直径有三尺二寸。用果核加上佐料做成羹汤,喝了可以延年益寿。核仁还可以治疗咳嗽。

2. Unusual Plants

Zhu Yu

On the mount of Zhao Yao grew a kind of grass which looked like Chinese chives but had green flowers. Eating it people would not feel hungry.

Bi Li

The grass called Bi Li could be found on the mount of Xiao Hua. It grew on the stone or along the wood. Those who take it may cure their heart troubles.

Striped Grass

Fu Yu mountain could see some grass with stripes. With red flowers and yellow fruits, the grass looked very much like the tongue of a baby. It could enable people to feel clear-minded and get rid of puzzlement.

Huang Guan

Huang Guan grass on the Zhu mountain was in the shape of the tree of heaven. Its leaves were similar to those of hemp. It had white flowers and black fruits. Dipping it into the water before taking a bath help to cure scabies.

Xun Cao

On the Fu mountain you could find a kind of grass called Xun Cao which had hemp-like leaves but square stalks. It had white flowers and dark fruits. Wearing it, people may prevent leprosy.

Gui Cao

The grass on the mount of Niu Shou was called Gui (meaning "ghost") Cao. It had red stalks and just like rice and millet, it sprouted ears and bore fruits. Eating it may relieve one's upset.

Wu Tiao

Wu Tiao grass on the Ku mountain had round leave, but without stalk. Taking it may prevent goitre.

Du Heng

On the mount of Tian Di grew certain grass called Du Heng which could be used to cure deep-rooted ulcer and goitre.

Millet-like Tree

Lun Zhe mountain could see a kind of millet-like tree, the grain of which was red. It gave out some pitch-dark juice which tasted like malt sugar. Eating it could get rid of hunger and fatigue. It could also be used to dye jade.

Huai Mu

On Zhong Qu mountain grew a kind of tree called Huai Mu, the leaves of which were round and the red fruits of which were as big as Chinese flowering quince. Eating the fruits could help to increase one's strength.

Wen Jing

Wen Jing tree on Fu Yu mountain had date-like fruits and could cure deafness.

Poplar-like Tree

Facing the North Sea was Bei Hao mountain on which grew a kind of poplar-like tree. It had red flowers and bore date-like, stoneless fruits which tasted sour and sweet. Eating the fruits could prevent malaria.

Qi Shu

Qi Shu on the mount of Dong Shi had red grain, giving out some red juice. Smearing a horse with such juice could make the horse liable to be tamed.

Huang Ji

On the mount of Ku grew a kind of tree called Huang Ji which had round leaves, yellow flowers and orchid-like fruits. If women happened to eat the fruits by mistake, they would never be able to have children.

Di Xiu

Surrounding Shao Shi mountain grew hundreds of grass and trees, among which was a tree called Di Xiu. Its leaves were similar to those of poplar and its branches grew crisscross. It had yellow flowers and black fruits. Eating the fruits may help to control one's anger.

Peach Tree

In the east there was a kind of fifty *zhang* (about 165 metres) high peach tree, the leaves of which were as long as eight *chi* (about 3 metres) and the diameter of the fruits of which was three *chi* and two *cun* (about 1 metres). Drinking the soup made of its cores along with some condiment could help to prolong one's life. The kernel could help to cure cough.

第 五 章
文明创始诸神

CHAPTER FIVE

GODS OF CIVILIZATION

一、有巢氏

　　大约在七十万年前，在中国这片土地上已有人类繁衍生殖。后来在很长的一段时间里，中国都处于石器时代。不过那时候的中国和现在却大不一样，气候更为温暖湿润，大地被森林与荒草覆盖，处处都有毒蛇猛兽，老虎、大象、鹿、豹成群地出没于山野密林之中。万物之灵的人类虽然已经觉察会用简单工具，而且常常猎杀野兽，但是也经常遭到野兽的袭击，因为与野兽比起来，人类实在太少了。他们的孩子被毒虫咬伤，妇女们也时遭禽兽侵袭。尤其是在那漫漫的黑夜里，当人熟睡的时候，人们往往成了食肉动物的佳肴。后来有一位圣明的人出现了。他教会人们在树上构建木屋，从那以后，人们就可以安睡而不必担心狼虫虎豹的搅扰了。于是人们把这位教给人类构木为巢的圣人尊为有巢氏。

1. You Chao, the God Who First Taught People to Build Shelters

About 700,000 years ago, humankind already existed in China, although for a very, very long time after that, China remained in the Stone Age. At that time, it was a completely different country. The climate was warmer and wetter and forests and wild grass covered the land. Among the mountains and dense woods, one could find poisonous snakes, wild beasts, tigers, elephants, deer, and leopards, moving to and fro in large groups. Even though human beings had alread learned to use simple tools and often hunted wild beasts, they were frequently attacked by these same beasts because, compared with them, humans were scarce. Poisonous insects hurt children and wild beasts attacked women, especially during long, dark nights. When people were fast asleep, carnivorous animals leapt at the opportunity to make them into delicious meals.

Later a wise man appeared and taught people to build wooden huts in the trees. From then on, people could sleep soundly without having to worry about wolves, tigers, leopards and insects. Not surprisingly, people respectfully called the wiseman You Chao, the Chinese for having nest, because it was You Chao who had taught people to build huts in the trees.

二、燧人氏

尽管在很久很久以前,人类便学会了用火,但是他们用的是自然火。天上的雷电燃着了野草树木,人们便取来火种,燃起篝火,回来炙烤食物并吓跑野兽。

在古代神话中,首先掌握自然火的火神是祝融。她居住在衡山上,是个老妇人,长着人一样的面孔,兽类的身躯,常乘二龙。是她给大地带来了光明。

后来人类文明发展了,他们学会了制做简陋的衣服,佩带装饰品,制做更应手的工具,同时也学会了用人工的方法取火。教会人们用人工取火的是燧人氏。据说在遥远的西方,有个太阳和月亮也无法到达的国度,叫做燧明国。那里既没有光辉的太阳、美丽的月亮和灿烂的星辰,所以也就无所谓昼夜,也没有春夏秋冬之分。然而那里却有一株大火树,叫做燧树,燧树盘曲万顷。有一种叫做鹗的鸟,在树上"咄咄"地凿着树干,它每凿一下,树上就迸发出灿烂的火花,燧明国的人便靠着这闪烁的火花照明。于是燧人氏就采集燧树的枝干并将它带回,教给人们钻木取火。

2. Sui Ren, Provider of Fire

Although human beings knew how to use fire a long, long time ago, they used only naturally occurring fire. Whenever thunder and lightening lit the wild grass and woods, people would get tinders and start fires to roast food and frighten away the wild beasts.

According to ancient myth, the first Goddess of Fire who could use naturally occurring fire was Zhu Rong. This old lady, who lived on Mount Heng, had the face of a human and the body of a beast and often could be seen riding two dragons. It was she who brought brightness to the earth.

Later, with civilization, humankind learned to make simple clothes. They wore ornaments and made better and more convenient tools. At the same time they learned how to make fire. It was Sui Ren who taught people how to make fire. It is said that in the remote west, a country existed where even the sun and moon could not reach. This country, Sui Ming, the country of brightness, had no bright sun, beautiful moon or bright stars. Although there was no night or day, no spring, summer, autumn, and winter, there was a large fire tree called Sui Shu. It covered an enormous area and an owl-like bird kept pecking at the tree, with a tap-tap-tap. When it would hit the tree with its beak, sparks would fly. People in the country of Sui Ming relied on these bright sparks for light. Later Sui Ren collected some branches from the flint tree and returned with it and taught people how to rub the tree to kindle fire.

三、伏羲氏

在非常遥远的地方,有一个快乐的国度。那里人人都生活得无忧无虑,逍遥自在。他们不懂得什么叫恐惧和嫉妒,也无所谓利害关系,他们没有爱和憎,生活恬淡,心地淳朴,在自然的怀抱中享受着人生,甚至连生死都置之度外。这些像神仙一样的人,却有着不寻常的本领。他们能飘飘然地在空中行走,完全和在陆地上一样,即使前面有云有雾,也遮不住他们的视线;即使风雨大作,雷霆轰鸣,他们仍然能够听到鸟儿的鸣转声和秋虫的叽叽声,这就是神话中的华胥国,也是伏羲的出生地。

伏羲的母亲被人称为神母。有一天她在华胥国游玩,突然有青虹从天而降缠绕着她,很久很久,方才消失,就这样她有了身孕。十二年后,生了伏羲;也有人说,她是踏了巨人的脚印而身怀有孕的;还有人说,伏羲的父亲是雷神。总之,他是知其母,而不知其父的。

伏羲生来就与凡人不同。他长着蛇的下身,龟齿龙唇,眉毛是白的,胡须直垂地面。半人半神的伏羲,常常沿着天梯上上下下,往来于人寰和天宫。后来据说他跟长着蛇身的女娲结成了夫妻。当时世上还没有人类,只有伏羲和女娲,就像西方的亚当和夏娃。他和女娲一同为后来出现的人类制定了婚娶制度。他还教会人们打猎,同时也教会人们畜养家畜,结网捕鱼,养蚕造丝。又用文字代替了结绳记事,发明了琴瑟,创始了音乐。他还懂得天文……总之,他对人类的贡献是很大的。

伏羲氏也被人们称为宓羲、庖牺等。人们相传他的种种发明与创造,实际上反映了中国新石器时代文明的进展程度。

3. Fu Xi, a Half Man and Half God Who Made Great Contributions to Humankind

In a very faraway place in a happy country lived a carefree people who enjoyed themselves greatly. They didn't know fear and jealousy and they didn't care about losses and gains. They felt neither love nor hatred, living quietly and peacefully. Being honest and unsophisticated, they enjoyed life surrounded by nature, giving no thought to life or death. These god-like people had some unusual skills. They could walk gracefully in the sky just as though they were walking on land and even the clouds and fog before them could not block their sight. They could even hear the chirps of birds and insects through heavy wind, rain and roaring thunder. This country, Hua Xu, was the birthplace of the god, Fu Xi.

Fu Xi's mother became pregnant with him in an unusal way. One day, while she was playing in the country of Hua Xu, suddenly a rainbow encompassed her, staying for a long time before it finally disappeared. And thus she became pregnant. Twelve years later she gave birth to Fu Xi. Some other people said that she stepped on the print of a giant and so became pregnant. Again some other people said that Fu Xi's father was the God of Thunder. Whichever story one believes, it is true that he knew

144

his mother but not his father.

Fu Xi was clearly no ordinary person. The lower part of his body was like that of a snake. He had turtle's teeth and a dragon's mouth. His eyebrows were white and his beard hung to the ground. Being half man and half god, Fu Xi went up and down the celestial ladder, going freely to and fro between the world of human beings and the celestial palace. It is said that later he married Nü Wa, who also had the body of a snake. At that time, Fu Xi and Nü Wa were only inhabitants of the earth, just as Adam and Eve had been in Western mythology. Later when the earth was peopled with humans, Fu Xi and Nü Wa created marriage customs. Fu Xi also taught people how to hunt, care and feed livestock, make fish nets, fish, keep silk worms and make silk. He also taught people how to use words to replace knots, the previous writing system. He invented musical instruments and created music. He also knew great deal about astronomy. In a word, he made great contributions to humankind. Fu Xi was also called, among other names, Fu Xi and Pao Xi. The myths about his different inventions and creations clearly reflect the development of civilization in China during the New Stone Age.

四、神 农 氏

神农氏也就是我们所说的炎帝。传说他的母亲是女登,是有娲氏家的姑娘。

神农的出生很神秘。一天女登到华阳去游玩,遇到了长着龙首的神而有了身孕,后来神农氏在江边出生长大,所以姓姜。他长着人身牛头,出生后的几个时辰便能说话,五天以后就能行走,七天以后,牙齿就长全了。到了三岁,便懂得种植五谷了。

在神农诞生的地方,有九眼水井,神农降生以后,这单个的九眼水井的水在地下就互相贯通了,若汲取其中一眼井的水,其余八眼的井水都会泛起波澜。

在神农之前,人类吃动物的肉,喝动物的血,也吃从树上采摘的果实,常生疾病。是神农教给人们开垦田土,合理利用土地,制造农具,并按时播种百谷。据说有一天,一只红色羽毛的鸟,嘴里衔一株九穗的禾稼从天空飞过,穗上的谷粒落在地下。神农把它一颗颗捡起,种在肥沃的黄土中,后来便长成了又高又大的庄稼。

神农不但是稼穑之神,还是医药之神。传说他有一条神鞭,他挥鞭抽击百草,便可以知道药草平、毒、温、寒等属性,然后采集来给人治病;也有人说,他还亲口去尝药草,为此他一天中了七十次毒。

过去只知道放牧的人们,学会了种植庄稼,人们的食物充足了,有些食物除满足自己所需也可将剩余同别人交换,于是神农又给人们建立了市场。由于实物交换的需要,神农又教给人们制造盛物的陶器,并在陶器上刻镂记号和花纹;由于农耕的需要,他还创立了历法。

神农氏的一切发明和创造,反映了六七十万年中国文明的进展情况。

4. Shen Nong, the God of Crops and Medicine

Shen Nong, also called Yan Di, was said to be the son of Nü Deng, a girl of the You Wa family.

Shen Nong's birth was very mysterious. One day while Nü Deng was playing in Hua Yang, she met a dragon-headed god, becoming pregnant by him. Later, Shen Nong was born, and because he was brought up by the river, his surname was Jiang, Chinese homonym for river. He had the body of a human and the head of an ox. Several hours after his birth, he could speak. Five days after his birth he could walk. Seven days later, he had a full mouth of teeth. By the time he was three, he knew how to plant crops.

The place where Shen Nong was born had nine wells. After Shen Nong's birth the water in these nine wells merged, so taking the water from one well would stir up the water in the other wells.

Before the time of Shen Nong, people ate fruit from the trees and raw animal meat, and drank animal blood. According to the myth, because of this, they often felt ill. Shen Nong changed all this by teaching people to plow the fields to make full use of the land, to make farm tools and to sow according to the climate. It is said that one day a bird with red feathers had a nine-eared seedling in its beak and while flying overhead, dropped the seeds on the ground. Shen Nong picked them up one by one and sowed them in the rich soil. Sometime later they grew into tall and healthy crops.

Shen Nong was not only the God of Crops, but also the God of Medicine. He was said to have had a magic whip. When he waved the whip to smash the grass he would know whether the herbs were mild, poisonous, moderate, or cooling. He could then choose appropriate herb for the particular disease. Some people said that he also tasted the herbs himself. In fact, one day he was poisoned seventy times while tasting the herbs.

People who had previously only known herding now learned how to plant crops, ensuring that adequate food was available. And in addition to their own food, people started trading the surplus with others. Shen Nong set up a market for the people. Because of the demand for exchanging goods, Shen Nong taught people to make pottery for containing goods and also showed them how to carve marks and signs on the pottery. Because of the need of farm work, he also created calendar.

All the inventions and creations of Shen Nong reflect the development of Chinese civilization six or seven hundred thousand years ago.

五、方　相

　　上古时代，人们除了受狼虫虎豹的危害，瘟疫和疾病也威胁着他们的生命，当时人们认为生病是由于疫鬼作祟。

　　相传北方有一位天神叫颛顼，是位本领高强的天帝，然而在他生的儿子中，有的死去却变成了疫鬼。一个死后，居住在江水，成了疟疾鬼。一个居住在若水，变成了魍魉，形象像个小孩子，红眼睛，长耳朵，长着漂亮的头发，红黑色的皮肤。他喜欢学人们讲话的声音来迷惑人。还有一个变成了小儿鬼，躲在人家屋里吓唬小孩。

　　当时有个驱逐疫鬼的神明，就是方相。他手掌上和长着熊一样的皮，四只眼睛中闪着金光，身着黑色上衣，红色裙子，一手拿着戈，一手拿着盾，有时也拿大斧，还用桃弓棘箭射杀疫鬼。他射出雨点般的箭，疫鬼一触，必死无疑；夜间，他举着明亮的火把，流星般地飞驰，把疫鬼逐往边远四方之地。

5. Fang Xiang, the God Who Was to Kill the Ghosts of Pestilence

In ancient times, apart from being attacked by wild beasts and poisonous insects, pestilence and disease also threatened people's lives. But at that time, people thought disease was a result of ghosts—the Ghosts of Pestilence.

It was said that in the north there was a very skillful god, Zhuan Xu. Unfortunately, though, some of his sons became the Ghosts of Pestilence after their deaths. One living in a river became the Ghost of Malaria; another living in the Ruo River became a demon who looked like a child with red eyes, long ears, lovely hair and reddish-black skin. He liked to imitate the sound of people to attract them. Another Zhuan Xu's son became a ghost that liked to hide in people's homes and frighten children.

During this time, the god, Fang Xiang had the task of ridding the world of the Ghosts of Pestilence. The skin of his palms was like that of a bear. Golden sparkles emanated from his four eyes. He wore black clothes, a red skirt and held a dagger in one hand and a shield in the other. On occasion, he held a big axe. He often carried his bow and arrow, always ready to shoot at the Ghosts of Pestilence should he happen upon them, and his arrows, just like raindrops, certainly killed them the minute they touched these terrible beings. At night he would hold a

151

bright torch and whirl it swiftly, and speed along like a meteor, scaring away these Ghosts of Pestilence to faraway places.

六、蚕 神

蚕女　明刊本《三教搜神大全》

在神农时代,人们的居住和饮食得到了改善,衣着也有了进步。我们的祖先最早制做衣服的原料是麻、革和蚕丝,在出土的文物中,就有麻布的印痕,也发现过新石器时代的革布残片。中国以蚕丝著称于世,是最早制作丝绸的国家,关于种桑养蚕,就有过这样的神话:在非常遥远的过去,人们聚族而居,因为没有共同的首领,各族间常常发生争战。有一家人养了个美丽的女儿。在她很小的时候,父亲就被邻族掠走。许多年过去了,音信全无,只有他的马天天在荒野上嘶叫悲鸣。女儿思念父亲,废寝忘食。为了安慰她,她的母亲便对部落中的人发誓说,如果有谁能把丈夫救出来,就把女儿嫁给谁。那匹马听到了她的话,嘶叫一声,挣脱缰绳,奔驰而走。几个月后,令人想不到的事情发生了,人们看到女孩的父亲骑着马回来了。一家人久别重逢,悲喜交集,从此过着和美安定的日子。

从那天起,那匹马却再也不肯进食,只是昼夜悲鸣。父亲问起缘由,母女二人也百思不得其解。后来母亲突然想到她当初对族人发誓时的情景。

父亲说："你是向人发誓，也不是对马发誓。人和马怎么能成亲呢？这匹马使我脱难，功劳是很大的，可是这个誓言不能作数。"

马听了以后，前蹄跪在地上哀嘶。父亲并未理会。马一跃而起，愤怒飞奔，追逐的人都被踢倒。父亲怒不可遏，便弯弓搭箭，把它射死，并且剥下马皮，晾在院中。碰巧女儿从院中经过，马皮突然腾空而起，将少女一卷而去。

几天以后，马皮又落在桑树上，少女已化做一只蚕，在树上吃着桑叶，后来吐丝作茧。从此以后人们便学会了养蚕，并用蚕丝织成美丽的丝绸。

少女的父母悔恨万分，非常想念女儿。一天，女儿穿着白色的丝裙，乘着被父亲射死的马，从彩云中凌空而降，对父母说，她已经成了长生不死的仙女，说罢便又乘马凌空而去。

6. The Goddess of Silk

In the time of Shen Nong, people's food and lodging, as well as their clothing, greatly improved. Our ancestors used fibre crops, leather and silk as the material for their clothing. Some unearthed relics even indicate the use of sack cloth while still others reveal remnants of leather cloth in the New Stone Age. China, the country which first made silk and long famous for it, has many myths about planting mulberry bushes and keeping silk worms.

In the very remote past, people lived in different clans because they had no common chief; wars often broke out among these clans. One such family had a lovely daughter whose father was taken away by a neighbouring clan when she was very young. Many years passed without any news about her father, but strangely, every day people could hear the neighing of his horse in the wilderness. The daughter sorely missed her father and sometimes she even refused to eat. In order to comfort her, her mother made a promise to the people in her clan that whoever could save her husband could marry her daughter. When the horse heard her promise, it rid itself of the constricting reins and with a neigh, ran away.

Several months later, the people of the girl's clan watched incredulously as the father returned on his horse. Feeling great joy at being together once again and sorrow at having been parted for so long, the family was once again whole and lived happily for a time after.

However, from the day of their return, the horse refused to eat a thing. He simply neighed sadly day and night. The father asked why, but at first, neither the mother nor the daughter could understand its strange behaviour. Then the mother remembered her promise to the people in her clan.

The father said, "The promise was made to the people not to the horse. How on earth could a horse and a human marry? This horse freed me from my terrible plight, and for this I am grateful, but this promise does not count."

On hearing this, the horse knelt on the floor and neighed sadly, but the father showed no sympathy so the horse jumped up and ran away angrily, kicking hard at all those who ran after it. The father was so angered that he took out his bow and shot the horse. Having killed it, the father peeled off its skin and left it to dry in the courtyard. While it was drying, the daughter happened to pass by and the horse skin suddenly jumped up, wrapped the girl up in its skin and flew away.

Several days later, the horse skin fell on a mulberry bush; the girl turned into a silkworm and ate mulberry leaves from the tree. Having had her fill, she spun a cocoon. From then on, people learned to keep silk worms and make beautiful silk from their cocoons.

The parents of the girl were deeply saddened and missed their daughter very much. One day the daughter, wearing a white silk dress, riding on the horse killed by her father, fell from the coloured clouds onto the ground. She informed her parents that she had become an immortal goddess, and after saying this flew away on the horse.

156

七、船神与车神

古时候的人想渡河、过海到神秘的地方去,所以发明了船。有人说有个叫共鼓的人,他看见空木头浮在水面,就挖空了树干造成了船只;有人说化狐看见游鱼划着水在水中戏游,于是便砍削木头做成船桨,划水行船。他们都被传为船神。

关于船的起源,还有一个美丽的传说。在浩淼无际的大海彼岸,有一片苍茫的大地,那里有宽广的大河。河的中央,有一个翠绿的岛子,上面有高大的树木和奇形怪状的石头。在岛子的南坡,有片青翠的竹林,那竹子长得很粗很粗,截取一段破开,就可以成一只载人的船了。

车子的构造由于比船的制做工艺较复杂,所以发明较船晚。据说车子的发明人是夏朝的奚仲。

有一天,奚仲正在草地上漫步,突然吹来一阵风,吹得干枯的蓬草飞快飘转,转得那么有趣,那么快。他就想,人如果也能走得那么快该有多好。于是在他的眼前便出现了车轮的形象,既而在他的脑海中又形成了车子的图案,这样他便开始制做车子了。

奚仲把木头弯曲成车轮,用直木做成车辕。他制做的车子的部件十分精良,构造坚固,运转自如。然后又驯服牛马拉车。

古人发明车子,恐怕比瓦特发明蒸汽机还要难呢,所以大家尊他为车神。

奚仲死后,葬在现在山东省薛城南二十五里处,那里有他的坟墓。而且在离现在山东省滕县六十里处是他试车的地方。据说在奚仲死后许多许多年,人们还能看见他试车时留下的轨辙呢。

7. The God of Boats and the God of Carts

In ancient times, people longed to cross rivers and seas to explore the unknown so they invented boats. According to some, the person, Gong Gu, after watching a piece of hollow wood floating on the water, hollowed out a tree trunk to create a "boat". Other people said that Hua Hu saw some fish cavorting in the water; their movements gave him an idea, so he cut some wood to make oars. Both were thought of as gods of boats by ancient people.

Another beautiful myth exists about the origin of the boat. On the other side of the boundless sea was a large area of land which contained a very broad river. In the middle of the river was a green island where some large trees and strangely shaped stones stood. At the south end of the island were some green bamboo woods where the bamboo was so thick that simply by cutting it in half, one could create a boat large enough to carry more than one person.

Because it is more complicated to make carts than boats, the creation of carts came later than that of boats. It is said that the creator of the cart was Xi Zhong during the Xia Dynasty.

One day, while Xi Zhong was taking a walk in the grasslands, a gust of wind came which made the dry and withering grass swirl swiftly round and round in a most interesting circular manner. He thought how wonderful it would be if people could walk so swiftly, and as he was thinking this, he imagined a wheel. Once he had the image of a wheel in his mind, he pictured an entire cart which he promptly started to make.

Xi Zhong bent the wood into the shape of a wheel and used straight wood to make cart shafts. The rest of the cart was made delicately but solidly with everything working smoothly. Once the cart was finished, Xi Zhong trained an ox and a horse to pull it.

It may have been more of a feat for ancient people to invent the cart than for Watt to invent the steam engine, so ancient people viewed Xi Zhong as the god of carts.

After his death, Xi Zhong was buried twenty-five *li* (about twelve kilometres) to the south of Xuecheng in Shandong Province, where people could find his tomb. And where he tested his cart, sixty *li* (thirty kilometres) from Teng County in Shandong Province, it is said that for years after his death, people could still see the wheel tracks.

八、陶神与铜神

在夏、商之前,中国是片快乐的土地,那时没有国王,也没有军队。一个氏族的人聚居在一起,几个氏族又联成一个部落。他们的首领都是选举产生的,大事都由智慧的长老决定。那时男女婚嫁也无须父母之命,媒妁之言,只是男孩子成年以后要嫁到女孩子家去。人们住在土墙草顶的圆屋子里,墙上的几个洞就算是窗户了。地下铺着席子和垫布,墙上挂着狩猎用的弓箭,屋外豢养着鸡狗,圈里喂养着牛羊。他们捕鱼,也用石锄、石刀种植蔬菜和谷子。到了赶集的日子,人们就到集市上去进行实物交换。除了妇女们戴的玉坠和骨珠之外,最引人注目的就要算是美丽的陶器了。

那时的人能够烧制瓮、盆、钵、碗等各种器皿,并在上面烧制美丽的花纹图案。中国的陶器到底是谁发明的,并没有确切的说法。除了前面所说的神农之外,有人说唐尧是陶神。又有人说是昆吾氏是陶神,说他除了制陶外,还发明了瓦,用来代替茅草铺盖屋顶。

从此以后,用了二百来万年石器的中国人,又开始冶炼金属了。这实在是件具有划时代意义的大事。在神话中,最先冶炼铜的神是蓐收。他的样子十分奇特,长着人的面孔,虎的爪子,还长条白色的尾巴。左耳上挂着蛇,手中拿把大斧,常常乘着两条龙。因为铜器非常贵重,除了做鼎一类的器具外,就是用来制做兵器,所以蓐收又被尊为刑法之神,他专替天帝讨伐为非作歹的人。

商周以后,中国文明进程加快。在都市中出现了高大的宫殿,富贵人家讲究的住宅,当然也出现了黑暗的监狱和毛骨悚然的刑具。严格的等级制度已经建立,礼仪戒律也愈加繁缛。与此同时,人们所享受的自由也就越来越少,先前那快乐的时代一去不复返了。

8. The God of Pottery and the God of Bronze

Before the Xia and Shang Dynasties, China was a happy land with neither king nor army to interfere. People of one clan lived together with several clans forming a tribe. Chiefs were all chosen and these wise elders made the important decisions of the community. Instead of obeying parents and matchmakers, a boy merely went to the girl's home once they mere married. People lived in round houses with earth walls and grass roofs. And the holes on the walls were their windows. On the floor they put mats and pads and on the walls they hung bows and arrows for hunting and outside the house they kept some roosters and dogs. In the pen, they fed oxen and sheep. They went fishing, planted vegetables and millet with stone hoes and stone knives, and when it was the day for them to go to a fair, they would go to a market to exchange their goods. Apart from the earings and bone-bead bracelets that women wore, the most attractive trading item was pottery.

People at that time could make all sorts of pottery containers such as jars, basins, and bowls, even adding beautiful designs to them. Nobody really knows who first created Chinese pottery. Apart from Shen Nong, mentioned above, some people said that Tang Yao was the God of Pottery, but it is also said that Kun Wu was. People said that apart from creating pottery, he also created tile to cover the roofs instead of cogon grass.

From then on, Chinese people who had used stone for twenty hundred thousand years began to smelt metal. This was an extremely significant development. According to the myth, Ru Shou was the god who first smelted bronze. He was very unusual looking the face of a human, the paws of a tiger and a white tail. On his left ear hung a snake, and he held a large axe in his hand. He was often seen riding two dragons. Because bronze was very precious, apart from some containers such as ancient cooking vessels, people only used it to make weapons; thus, Ru Shou was also regarded as the God of Punishment, dealing with evil people for the King of Heaven. After the Shang and Zhou Dynasties, Chinese civilization developed rapidly. In the cities, tall palaces and luxurious houses for the wealthy appeared, but along with them, dark prisons and frightening tools of punishment also appeared. A strict hierarchy was set up and rites became more and more complicated. At the same time, people enjoyed less freedom and the happy and carefree times were gone forever.

九、万能之神

　　在文明发展的进程中，上古人创造了各种各样的工具，也创造了与之相应的神明形象而加以颂扬。这些大智大慧，超凡入圣的神明集中地表现了上古人民的才智和理想。在诸多神明之中，巧倕是非常引人注目的。

　　据说巧倕能制做许多种农具，还会造钟、鼓、磬等乐器。他还创造了规矩准绳。因为他善分辨各种材料的优劣而充当了工匠的总管。他是机械方面的神圣。

　　与巧倕齐名的是先通，他也是一位杰出的智慧之神，据说他知道河水、海水的数量，知道山上有多少块石头；他不但能听懂大地上所有人的语言，还能辨出林中鸟儿啼叫声的意思。这实在是位万能之神。然而他样子却很奇怪，身高一丈，腰围九尺，脚下踏着龟和蛇，头上顶着神鸟，用一只手按着一条白虎。人们都很希望能见到他。因为如果见到先通，而能向他行礼，傻子也会变成聪明人。

9. Omnipotent Gods

With the development of civilization, ancient people invented all sorts of tools and at the same time created many images of gods to praise. These wise supermen embodied the wisdom and ideals of ancient people. Among these many supermen, Qiao Chui was particularly special.

It is said that Qiao Chui could make many kinds of farm tools. He could also make musical instrument such as bells, drums, and chime stones. He also invented standards. Because he was very good at distinguishing the quality of all sorts of materials, he became the head of the craftsmen and was considered the wise man of machinery and technology.

Xian Tong was as well known as Qiao Chui and was also an outstanding god of wisdom. It is also said that he knew the quantity of water in rivers and seas and how many stones the mountains held. Not only could he understand all the languages of the world but he could also interpret the birds' chirpings in the woods. Although he was most decidedly an omnipotent god, he looked exceedingly strange. He was one *zhang* (3.33 metres) tall with a waistline of nine *chi* (three metres). A turtle and a snake were attached under his feet while on his head was a magic bird. Under his hand was a white tiger. People were always eager to see him because whoever could see him and bow to him would become clever even if he were a fool.

十、天文之神

　　中国古代很久就有非常发达的农业,除了神农氏之外,出现过许多农艺家,例如姜嫄的儿子,也是周民族的始祖后稷就很善于稼穑耕耘,据说他教会人们播种百谷,所以人们尊他为天地之主。他还教会人们用牛耕地。由于农业生产的需要,历法也很早就在中国出现,人们说最早的日历发明者是炎帝,也有说是唐尧。到了夏朝历法就相当完善了。那时,人们不再孤立地研究太阳、月亮、星辰,而是从日出月落,星辰运转把许多天文现象联系起来去发现总结规律。所以就出现了管理日月星辰运行和止息的神明。

　　有一个神叫石夷,他住在天的西北角,主管着日月出没时间的长短。还有一个神明叫鹓,他住在女和月母国,据说也掌管日月,让它们不间断地出没,并主司着出没时间的长短。还有人说,在大荒之中,有一座山,叫日月山,山上有位神明,长着人的面孔,但没有手臂,两脚反搭在头上,他叫嘘,他也是掌管日月出没的神明。

10. The God of Astronomy

Agriculture was very well developed in ancient China. Apart from Shen Nong, there appeared many agronomists such as Hou Ji, the son of Jiang Yuan, who was also the ancestor of the Zhou clan. He was very good at planting crops. It is said that he taught people to sow crops which is why he was worshipped as the master of Earth and Sky. He also taught people to plow fields using oxen. Because of the demand of agricultural production, the calendar appeared very early in China. People said that the first writer of the calendar was Yan Di while others said that it was Tang Yao. By the Xia Dynasty, the calendar was more exact as people no longer studied the sun, moon and stars separately. Instead, they took astronomy very seriously; by studying the rising and setting sun and moon and the movements of the stars, they discovered their regular patterns. From this there appeared the god who was in charge of the movement of the sun, the moon and the stars.

The god, Shi Yi, who lived in the northwest of the sky was in charge of the duration of the sun and moon's rising and setting. Another god, Yuan, lived in the country of Nü He Yue Mu. He was also said to be in charge of the sun and moon, letting them come and go continuously but governing the duration. It was said that in the open country, Mount Ri Yue, the sun and moon, had an armless and legless god with the face of a human. He hung his two feet on his head. He was called Xu. He was also the god in charge of the rising and setting of the sun and the moon.

十一、画神与字神

在中国很早就出现了绘画，它的诞生大约在旧石器时代后期，然后不断发展。现在我们还能看到在岩石上遗留的图画。

有人说苗龙是绘画的鼻祖，也有人说舜帝的妹妹嫘创始了绘画，所以称她做画嫘。除此之外，还有许多别的人。可见绘画的创始是有一定群众性的。

中国文字的出现也很早。最初，用结绳的方法，记录生活中的重大事件。也有人用在木头上刻些道道来帮助记忆。后来就采用了绘画的方式，那些帮助记忆的图绘越来越简化，变成些横勾撇捺，又加上些其它因素，就演化成了文字。

早在原始公社时期，中国人便使用着一种简单的文字，到了商朝，中国文字不但出现，而且已相当发达了。然而在神话中，人们却把文字的发现说得神秘而又奇妙。他们说文字是由仓颉创造的。仓颉是天降的神，他长着四只眼睛，神光四射。他的长相很像龙。当他还是一个婴儿的时候，就喜欢用东西东涂西抹。长大以后，便研究天地万物的变化。夜晚，他抬头仰望奎星的形状；白天又去考察龟背上的花纹，飞鸟的羽毛以及山川的起伏和气势。他尤其善于观察鸟兽行走的踪迹，然后便在自己的手掌上涂涂画画，从而创造了文字。

文字创造以后，天下所有的事物都可以记载下来，伟大的业绩也可以载入史册，人间是非曲直，也可以得到表现，这真是惊天动地的大事。为此，天上掉下了粟米，鬼魂们在夜晚哭泣起来，连称雄一时的蛟龙也潜入水底躲藏起来。

11. The God of Paintings and the God of Characters

Long long ago in China, in the latter part of the Old Stone Age, paintings first appeared and from then continued to develop. Even now, we can see some of these early pictures left on the rocks.

According to some, Miao Long was the originator of paintings while others said that it was Lei, the sister of Shun Di, who created paintings. Thus, people called her Hua Lei since *hua* means painting in Chinese. Many others were involved as well so we can see that the creation of paintings had a broad foundation involving many people.

Chinese characters also appeared a long, long time ago. At first, people recorded the important events of their lives by tying knots and other people cut stripes on wood to help them remember things. Later, they drew pictures to remember things and gradually the pictures became more and more simplified. After some time, the horizontal stroke, the hook, the left falling stroke and the right falling stroke, so characteristic of Chinese writing, emerged and along with other features, they became characters.

Even in early primitive communities, Chinese people used a simple form of characters. During the Shang Dynasty, Chinese characters were very well developed, yet according to Chinese mythology, people infused the creation of characters with great significance, colour and mystery. They said that Cang Jie, a god who came from heaven, created the characters. He had four eyes from which shone magic light. He looked very much like a dragon. As a baby he loved to draw and when he grew up, he studied the changes of all living things in the sky and on the earth. At night he looked up at the shape of some star and during the day, he observed the designs on the turtle's back, the feathers of flying birds and the shapes and movements of mountains and rivers. He was particularly good at observing the trails of birds and beasts. He would then draw them in his own palm, and doing so, he created characters.

After the creation of characters, people could record everything that was occurring around them. Great historic deeds could also be recorded as well as the rights and wrongs of the world. It was indeed an event of monumental significance. In fact, because of this, millet dropped from the sky, ghosts cried at night and even a powerful floodcreating dragon dove into the water to hide.

十二、音乐与舞蹈之神

在漫长的封建社会里，艺术家的地位非常低下。王公贵族借音乐舞蹈寻欢作乐，而民间的音乐舞蹈则不被正统舆论所认可，所以一般人很少有机会开怀歌舞。岂不知在无拘无束的上古时代音乐与舞蹈非常发达。每当月明星稀的夜晚，劳动之余，人们便擂鼓作乐，手之舞之，足之蹈之，边歌边舞往往通宵达旦。同时，民间也流传着关于歌舞的神话。据说黄帝命令伶伦造乐律，伶伦便走到翠谷中选取竹子。他按一定的长短比例把竹子截成十二根竹管，然后便来到昆仑山麓。那里栖着五彩羽毛的凤凰。他想根据凤凰鸣叫的声音来区别竹管的律调。一天，凤凰果然叫了起来，雄的叫了六声，雌的也叫了六声。于是伶伦便定下了十二种不同的律调。

鼓在原始社会中有着重要的地位。不论是在娱乐，还是在祭祀的时候，人们都会擂鼓作乐。在战场上，两军对垒也会战鼓隆隆。中国在上古时代便发明了鼓。

在神话中，天帝颛顼曾让鱓奏乐，于是鱓就躺在地下用尾巴敲打自己的肚皮，发出"英英"的声音。舜的臣子夔也造鼓，他把麋皮蒙在缶上敲击，同时还打击石片，模仿天国玉磬的声音。

帝江是舞蹈之神。他的样子很怪，像只黄袋子，然而却发散着红光。他长着四只翅膀，六只脚，可是人们却看不清他的面目。

舞蹈之神为什么会是这副模样呢？也许是当时的艺术家为了戏剧效果而进行的化装或做的道具。据说夏禹的儿子启也是舞蹈艺术家。他的母亲变成了块石头，裂开以后生下了他。他向往天上的歌舞，于是便上天把歌舞偷了来。也有人说他是送了三个美女给天帝而换取了歌舞，然后在高山上演奏。他还在平旷的地方跳舞。跳舞时站在搭着高篷的车子上，身上佩戴着玉璜，左手拿着羽毛，右手握着玉环，还驾着两条龙。从这些传说中足以想见当年歌舞粗犷豪迈的气势了。

12. The Gods of Music and Dance

In feudal society, although the nobility valued music and dance and gained great pleasure from it, the musicians had a very low social position. Folk music and folk dancing, on the other hand, were not accepted at all by the orthodoxy so ordinary people had little chance to sing and dance freely. However, in carefree ancient times, the situation was different; music and dance were highly developed and respected. In the evenings after a long day's work, under the moon and bright stars, people beat drums, sang and danced all night long. At the same time, many myths and legends were told about singing and dancing.

It was said that Huang Di ordered Ling Lun to create musical tones so he went to a green valley to choose some bamboo which he cut, according to careful proportions, into twelve bamboo pipes of different lengths. Then he went to Mount Kunlun where the colorfully feathered phoenix lived. Ling Lun wanted to match the notes of the bamboo according to the call of the phoenix. After waiting some time, one day the phoenix called at last. The male called six times and so did the female; thus Ling Lun created twelve different tones.

Drums played a very important role in primitive society. Whenever people wanted to enjoy themselves or make a sacrifice, they would beat drums and play music. On the war field war drums sounded when the two sides faced each other. According to mythology, drums were created in very ancient times. The King of Heaven, Zhuan Xu, asked Shan to play music so Shan lay on the floor and beat his own belly with his tail, making a thumping, hollow sound, One of Shun's subjects, Kui, also created drums. He covered a vat with elk skin and beat it, and at the same time, he knocked on a piece of stone to imitate the sound of the jade chimestone in the celestial palace.

Di Jiang was the God of Dance. He looked exceedingly strange—like a glowing yellow sack. Although we know he had four wings and six feet, people could not see him clearly. How could the God of Dance look like this? Perhaps the artists at that time simply imagined him like that or created a stage property for dramatic effect. It was said that Qi, the son of Xia Yu, was also a dancer. His mother turned into a stone and when the stone cracked he emerged from it. Apparently he greatly appreciated the singing in Heaven and longed to have it for himself, so he went there to steal it. Others said that he sent three beautiful girls to the King of Heaven in exchange. He played music on the high mountains and danced on the open plains. When he danced he also stood on a cart with a high awning. He wore jade pendant, held a feather in his left hand and a jade ring on his right. He also rode two dragons. From these stories we can well imagine the bold and unconstrained mometum of the singing and dancing at that time.

十三、音乐家夔

　　夔本是山的精怪。他长得像头青牛，可是没有角，而且他只有一条腿。生活在山林中的夔，早上听着鸟儿的鸣啭，夜晚听着虫儿的呢喃。伴着他的还有风声、雨声、树叶的沙沙声及山溪流淌的潺潺声。于是用心专一地品味体察这些声音而创始了音乐。他演奏的音乐引来了百鸟，甚至连百鸟之王的凤凰也飞来倾听。接着，山林中的野兽也聚集而来，随着音乐的节拍手舞足蹈，形成了林中空前的盛会。后来，为了仿效这次鸟兽盛会，人类也常常头戴羽毛，身披兽皮，并装上兽尾，在音乐的伴奏下跳舞。

　　天上的大神，人间的帝王——黄帝了解到夔的音乐才能后把他召进宫来演奏音乐。夔引吭高歌，并把麋皮蒙在缶上当鼓敲击，同时还拍打石片，听上去简直跟天乐一般。黄帝十分高兴。黄帝尤其喜欢夔所造的鼓。

　　当时部落之间战争频繁，在战场上战鼓一擂，便会军心大振，队伍所向披靡。

　　黄帝要和蚩尤打仗了。这是一场规模空前的大战。夔得知这一消息后，便趴在地上两眼直流泪水。人们问他为什么要哭。他说："黄帝就要打仗了。"人们说："可是黄帝打的是蚩尤啊！"夔说："打仗需要战鼓，黄帝定会用我的皮制做战鼓。"

　　果然，一天夜里，黄帝命人把夔杀死，用他的皮做了一面战鼓。

　　在双方对垒、杀声震天的战场上擂动了这面战鼓，远近五百里都能听见，于是黄帝军威大振。虽然蚩尤的八十一个兄弟个个铜头铁额，并能以砂石为食，而蚩尤本人也长了八条臂膀，有坚不可摧的二寸长的牙齿，而面对战鼓震天的黄帝部族也难前进半分。黄帝这方一连擂鼓九次,蚩尤的军队便瘫软如泥,被黄帝的部下杀死。

蚩尤死之后,到东海做了雷神。他的声音就像隆隆的战鼓,一切妖魔鬼怪一听到便都逃之夭夭。

13. The Musician Kui

Kui was a one-legged monster of the mountain who looked like a hornless black ox. Living in the mountain woods, Kui listened to the chirping of the birds in the morning and of the insects at night. The sound of the wind and rain, the rustling of the leaves in the trees and the murmuring of the mountain streams also surrounded him. He listened attentively feeling the music in these various sounds, and finally from this, created his own music. His music attracted hundreds of birds. Even the phoenix, the king of the birds, flew to listen to him. Then the animals in the mountain woods gathered and danced to the rhythm of the music which was indeed an grand and unprecedented occasion. Later, to imitate this grand occasion, people danced to the music, wearing feather, animal skins, and animal tails.

Huang Di, the God of Heaven and the King of the World learned about the musical talent of Kui so he summoned him to the palace to play. Kui sang in a joyful, full voice and he also beat on an elk-skin covered vat. At the same time he beat the stone piece, recreating the sound of celestial music. The music, and the drumming in particular, made Huang Di extremely happy.

At this time, wars often broke out among tribes. On the battlefield, the moment the war drum was beaten the morale of the troops would be raised and soldiers would sweep all obstacles away.

At one time, Huang Di decided to enter battle against Chi You, who had plotted a rebellion against him. It would prove to be a very bitter fight. On realizing what he was about to face, Kui lay face down on the floor and his eyes filled with tears. When people asked him why he was crying, he replied, "Huang Di is going to wage war." People said in amazement, "It is none other than Chi You who Huang Di wants to fight." At this point, Kui retorted, "Fighting needs a war drum and Huang Di will definitely want to use my skin to made a war drum."

As expected, one night Huang Di ordered someone to kill Kui and made a war drum with his skin.

The war drum was beaten in the raging battlefield where the two sides faced each other. The sound of the drum was so powerful it could be heard five hundrd *li* (two hundred and fifty kilometres) away thus giving Huang Di's troops a great boost. Even though the eighty one brothers of Chi You all had bronze heads and iron foreheads and could eat sand and stones and Chi You himself had eight arms and indestructible teeth two *cun* (eight inches) long, they were no match for the troops with the beating war drum. In fact, Huang Di's troops beat the drums nine times at one sitting rendering Chi You's troops as weak and limp as mud and thus Huang Di's troops killed Chi You's.

After Kui died, he went to the East Sea to become the God of Thunder. His voice was just like the beating war drum, and all the demons, monsters and ghosts made their getaway when they heard his sound.

十四、灶神与门神

　　上古时代的人学会造屋以后，又渐渐由半坡时期圆形的茅屋发展成有院墙四合院。不但有了房门，还有了院门。人们在门上贴上门神像。

　　门神并不是门的创造者，而是门户的守卫者。关于门神的神话中说，沧海之中有一座名叫度朔的山，山上有株大桃树，树上有只玉鸡。太阳一出来，

神荼郁垒　明刊本《三教搜神大全》

它就喔喔啼叫。这株桃树巨大无比,枝叶覆压三千里。树枝间有道鬼门,是万鬼出没的地方。此门有两位神人把守。一位叫神荼,一位叫郁垒,他们管理着群鬼,据说他们是兄弟俩。如果有的鬼做了害人的事,这两位神人就把他们绑起来喂虎。于是神荼和郁垒就成了门户之神。老百姓把他们的像贴在自己家的门上,还画上一只老虎来恐吓为非作歹的鬼魅。

关于灶神,人们有许多传说。一个小小的炉灶,但对人们来说,它显得十分重要。有人说,黄帝死后成了灶神。也有人说,炎帝死后成了灶神。还有人说,灶神是最先利用自然火的祝融。

灶神　明刊本《三教搜神大全》

民间供灶神的习俗,在中国一直很流行,不过灶神像已是个戴着乌纱的官吏。人们说,在腊月二十四日,灶神就要回到天帝那里汇报人间的事情,尤其是人们的过失。天帝还根据罪过情节的轻重，对有过失的人进行不同的处罚。轻者让他少活一百天，重者少活三百天。所以下民对灶神抱有一种畏惧心理。每当腊月二十三日，人们便纷纷祭灶，除了供献上各种美味佳肴，还特地为灶神买来麦芽做的辞灶糖瓜，目的是让灶神吃了把牙粘住，这样他就无法向天帝做小汇报了；也有人贴出"上天言好事""下地降吉祥"的对联。

社会进化了，人间世界改变了，人们所想像的超自然的世界也发生了变化。对于灶神，人们不像对女娲、伏羲那样又敬又爱，因而就想出了这种奇特的办法对付他。

14. The Kitchen God and the Door Gods

After people in ancient times learned how to build shelters, houses developed from circular grass huts in the period of Ban Po to rectangular buildings with courtyards. People placed pictures of door gods on both their house doors and courtyard doors.

The Door Gods were not the creators of the door but the doorkeepers. In the door god myth, a giant peach tree, whose branches and leaves extended three thousand *li*, grew on Mount Du Shuo in the blue sea. Perched on this tree was a jade rooster which would crow whenever the sun rose. Among the branches stood a ghost's door, the place for all the ghosts to come and go. Two gods, Shen Shu and Yu Lü who were said to be brothers and in charge of all the ghosts, kept guard at this door. If any ghosts harmed people in any way, Shen Shu and Yu Lü would tie them up and feed them to tigers, and so it was that these two became Door Gods. People put up their pictures on their front doors and drew tigers to frighten away evil ghosts.

People had many stories about the Kitchen God. Even though the kitchen hearth was very small, it was very important to everyone. Some said that Huang Di became the Kitchen God after his death; others suggested that it was Yan Di, but still others said that the Kitchen God was Zhu Rong, the first person to make use of natural fire.

Worshipping the Kitchen God had long been popular in China, but ultimately the image of the Kitchen God had become an official wearing a black gauze cap. People said that on the twenty-fourth day of the twelfth month of the lunar year, the Kitchen God would go back to the King of Heaven to report things on Earth, especially people's faults. Then the King of Heaven would punish faulty people according to the degree of the mistakes. People who committed the least serious offenses would have a mere one hundred days taken off their lives while those who made serious errors would have three hundred days taken away. Not surprisingly, everybody was afraid of the Kitchen God.

On the twenty-third day of the twelfth month of the lunar year, people would worship the kitchen hearth. Apart from offering all sorts of delicious foods, they also bought the Kitchen God some maltose so that his teeth would stick together and he would be unable to say anything bad about people to the King of Heaven. Some other people put up an antithetical couplet written on a scroll with the words, "Going to the sky to say good things; Coming to the earth to bring good luck."

As society developed, humankind changed greatly and so too did people's ideas about the supernatural world. People did not respect and love the Kitchen God as they did Nü Wa and Fu Xi; therefore they thought of this highly unusual way to deal with him.

附　录

总　词　汇　表

APPENDIX

GLOSSARY

第一章

一、

1. 开天辟地	kāitiān-pìdì		separate heaven from earth；since the beginning of history
2. 凝视	níngshì	（动）	stare at
3. 灿烂	cànlàn	（形）	bright；magnificent
4. 宇宙	yǔzhòu	（名）	cosmos；universe
5. 极限	jíxiàn	（名）	the limit
6. 延伸	yánshēn	（动）	extend；stretch
7. 主宰	zhǔzǎi	（名、动）	master；dominate；control
8. 创始	chuàngshǐ	（动）	initiate；originate
9. 浑沌	húndùn	（形）	chaos
10. 孕育	yùnyù	（动）	be pregnant with
11. 懊恼	àonǎo	（形）	annoyed
12. 烦闷	fánmèn	（形）	unhappy；upset
13. 浊	zhúo	（形）	muddy；murky
14. 筋脉	jīnmài	（名）	veins
15. 骨髓	gǔsuí	（名）	marrow
16. 雨露	yǔlù	（名）	rain and dew
17. 甘霖	gānlín	（名）	timely rainfall
18. 五彩缤纷	wǔcǎi-bīnfēn		colourful

二、

1. 苍茫	cāngmáng	（形）	vast and hazy
2. 辽阔	liáokuò	（形）	boundless；vast
3. 扶桑	fúsāng	（名）	mulberry

4.	桑葚	sāngshèn	（名）	the fruit of mulberry tree
5.	栖	qī	（动）	rest；perch
6.	奔驰	bēnchí	（动）	run quickly
7.	游荡	yóudàng	（动）	roam；wander
8.	炙烤	zhìkǎo	（动）	scorch
9.	善	shàn	（动）	be good at
10.	射	shè	（动）	shoot

三、

1.	晶莹	jīngyíng	（形）	sparkling and crystal-clear
2.	婆娑	pósuō	（形）	whirling；dancing
3.	遨游	áoyóu	（动）	roam；travel
4.	癞蛤蟆	làiháma	（名）	good
5.	豹	bào	（名）	leopard
6.	尾	wěi	（名）	tail
7.	掌管	zhǎngguǎn	（动）	administer
8.	瘟疫	wēnyì	（名）	pestilence
9.	刑罚	xíngfá	（名）	penalty；punishment
10.	觅	mì	（动）	look for
11.	慷慨	kāngkǎi	（形）	generous
12.	疙瘩	gēda	（名）	a swelling on the skin
13.	寂寞	jìmò	（形）	lonely

四、

1.	温柔	wēnróu	（形）	gentle and soft
2.	纺纱	fǎngshā	（动）	spin
3.	织布	zhībù	（动）	weave
4.	梳妆	shūzhāng	（动）	dress and make up
5.	打扮	dǎbàn	（动）	dress up
6.	欢娱	huānyú	（形）	happy；joyous
7.	孤独	gūdú	（形）	lonely；solitary

8. 辛劳	xīnláo	(形)	toil;pains
9. 嬉戏	xīxì	(动)	play
10. 贪恋	tānliàn	(动)	be reluctant to part with
11. 荒废	huāngfèi	(动)	neglect
12. 责备	zébèi	(动)	reproach;blame
13. 柔嫩	róunèn	(形)	tender
14. 纤细	xiānxì	(形)	very thin
15. 梭子	suōzi	(名)	shuttle
16. 耕作	gēngzuò	(动)	to farm;to till
17. 徘徊	páihuái	(动)	pace up and down
18. 喜鹊	xǐquè	(名)	magpie
19. 轻盈	qīngyíng	(形)	slim and graceful

五、

1. 翅膀	chìbǎng	(名)	wing
2. 驱逐	qūzhú	(动)	drive out
3. 妖邪	yāoxié	(名)	monster
4. 丑陋	chǒulòu	(形)	ugly
5. 逃窜	táocuàn	(动)	run away
6. 麻雀	máquè	(名)	sparrow
7. 鹿	lù	(名)	deer
8. 蛇	shé	(名)	snake
9. 龟	guī	(名)	turtle
10. 祭祀	jìsì	(动)	offer sacrifices to goods or ancestors
11. 卜	bǔ	(动)	divine
12. 鳞甲	línjiǎ	(名)	scale and shell
13. 祀奉	sìfèng	(动)	worship

六、

1. 巍峨	wēi'é	(形)	lofty
2. 苍郁	cāngyù	(形)	verdant

3.	夭折	yāozhé	（动）	die young
4.	仪态万方	yítài-wànfāng		(of a beauty) appear in all her glory
5.	赋	fù	（名）	poetic essay
6.	泛滥	fànlàn	（动）	overflow
7.	治理	zhìlǐ	（动）	control；harness
8.	水患	shuǐhuàn	（名）	flood
9.	骤起	zhòu qǐ		suddenly arise
10.	悬崖	xuányá	（名）	cliff
11.	震荡	zhèndàng	（动）	shake
12.	崩塌	bēngtā	（动）	crumble
13.	凿通	záo tōng		chisel open；drive through
14.	白鹤	báihè	（名）	white crane
15.	谒访	yèfǎng	（动）	call on (a superior or an older person)
16.	琼楼玉宇	qiónglóu-yùyǔ		magnificent building
17.	属神	shǔshén	（名）	subordinate；dependent god
18.	眺望	tiàowàng	（动）	look into the distance

七、

1.	披	pī	（动）	wear；throw on
2.	羽毛	yǔmáo	（名）	feather
3.	盘旋	pánxuán	（动）	to circle；to wheel
4.	袒露	tǎnlù	（动）	expose；to bare
5.	乳房	rǔfáng	（名）	breast
6.	怀孕	huáiyùn	（动）	be pregnant
7.	窥探	kuītàn	（动）	peep
8.	伺机	sìjī	（副）	await an opportunity
9.	滴	dī	（动）	to drop
10.	计谋	jìmóu	（名）	plot；sheme

190

11.	晾	liàng	（动）	dry in the sun
12.	怏怏	yàngyàng	（副）	sullen

八、

1.	荒原	huāngyuán	（名）	wilderness
2.	萋萋	qīqī	（形）	luxuriant
3.	筑巢	zhù cháo		built a nest
4.	孵化	fūhuà	（动）	hatch
5.	崇拜	chóngbài	（动）	worship
6.	牲畜	shēngchù	（名）	livestock
7.	礼拜	lǐbài	（动）	worship；pay homage to
8.	庄稼	zhuāngjia	（名）	crops
9.	畏惧	wèijù	（名）	be afraid of
10.	索取	suǒqǔ	（名）	take away
11.	幽冥	yōumíng	（名）	the nether world
12.	偶尔	ǒu'ěr	（副）	once in the while；occasionally
13.	闪烁	shǎnshuò	（动）	glisten
14.	蓬松	péngsōng	（形）	fluffy
15.	狐狸	húli	（名）	fox

九、

1	浑身	húnshēn	（名）	the whole body
2.	推崇	tuīchóng	（动）	worship
3.	白斑	báibān	（名）	white spot
4.	景仰	jǐngyǎng	（动）	admire
5.	赞诵	zànsòng	（动）	praise
6.	妍媚冶艳	yánmèi yěyàn	（形）	extremely delicate and charming
7.	烟波浩淼	yānbō hàomiǎo		a wide expanse of mist-covered waters

十、

1.	鳖	biē	（名）	soft-shelled turtle

2.	从事	cóngshi	（名）	subordinate
3.	乌贼鱼	wūzéiyú	（名）	inkfish
4.	小吏	xiǎolì	（名）	official
5.	统率	tǒngshuài	（动）	command
6.	属下	shǔxià	（名）	subordinate
7.	威风	wēifēng	（形）	imposing
8.	随从	suícóng	（名）	servant；suite
9.	贪财	tāncái	（动）	be greedy for money
10.	覆没	fùmò	（动）	overturn
11.	抢掠	qiǎnglüè	（动）	rob
12.	肝胆	gāndǎn	（名）	heroic spirit
13.	璧玉	bìyù	（名）	a kind of jade
14.	毫无惧色	háowú jùsè		be not afraid at all
15.	颠簸	diānbǒ	（动）	bump
16.	宝剑	bǎojiàn	（名）	sword
17.	凶猛	xiōngměng	（形）	fierce
18.	不可一世	bùkè-yīshì		consider oneself unexcelled in the world
19.	鄙夷不屑	bǐyí bùxiè		scornfully
20.	弹	tán	（动）	bounce
21.	厚颜无耻	hòuyán-wúchǐ		shameless
22.	羞辱	xiūrǔ	（名）	insult；humiliation
23.	砸	zá	（动）	break
24.	粉碎	fěnsuì	（动）	smash
25.	惜财	xīcái		to treasure wealth
26.	屈服	qūfú	（动）	yield

十一、

1.	粼粼	línlín	（形）	clear
2.	窈窕	yǎotiǎo	（形）	(of a moman) gentle and graceful
3.	婀娜多姿	ēnuó duōzī		(of a woman's bearing) graceful

4. 面颊	miànjiá	（名）	face
5. 润如出水芙蓉	rùn rú chū shuǐ fúróng		be as exquisite as a lotus
6. 溺死	nìsǐ	（动）	be drowned
7. 螭	chī	（名）	a kind of dragon
8. 荷叶	héyè	（名）	lotus leaf
9. 巅	diān	（名）	top of mount
10. 瑰丽华美	guīlì huáměi		magnificent
11. 贝	bèi	（名）	shell
12. 绘	huì	（动）	to paint
13. 漆	qī	（动）	to paint
14. 品行不端	pǐnxíng bùduān		ill behave
15. 灵芝	língzhī	（名）	glossy ganoderma
16. 蚌壳	bàngké	（名）	clam shell
17. 落落寡欢	luòluò-guǎhuān		dejectedly
18. 惆怅	chóuchàng	（形）	upset
19. 一见钟情	yījiàn-zhōngqíng		fall in love at first sight
20. 窥探	kuītàn	（动）	peep；spy upon
21. 瞎	xiā	（动）	blind
22. 告状	gàozhuàng	（动）	complain
23. 偏袒	piāntǎn	（动）	to favour
24. 安分守己	ānfèn-shǒujǐ		know one's place
25. 侵犯	qīnfàn	（动）	intrude
26. 兽	shòu	（名）	beast

十二、

1. 巍峨壮丽	wēi'é zhuànglì		magnificent
2. 瑶	yáo	（名）	jade
3. 撞大运	zhuàng dà yùn		try one's luck
4. 滑腻	huánì	（形）	smooth
5. 漫不经心	mànbùjīngxīn		careless

193

十三、

1. 远古	yuǎngǔ	（名）	remote antiquity
2. 广袤	guǎngmào	（形）	boundless
3. 神祇	shénqí	（名）	gods
4. 捏	niē	（动）	mould
5. 飞溅	fēijiàn	（动）	splash
6. 生育	shēngyù	（动）	bear
7. 繁衍	fányǎn	（动）	multiply
8. 奉	fèng	（动）	regard
9. 祭祀	jìsì	（动）	worship
10. 万物竞萌	wànwù jìng méng		all living things are about to blossom
11. 情侣	qínglǔ	（名）	lover
12. 幽僻	yōupì	（形）	quiet
13. 履行	lǚxíng	（动）	go through
14. 法律	fǎlǜ	（名）	law
15. 仪式	yíshì	（名）	ceremony；rite
16. 擎持	qíngchí	（动）	prop up
17. 拉拽	lāzhuài	（动）	pull
18. 燃（烧）	rán(shāo)	（动）	burn
19. 乱窜	luàncuàn	（动）	run
20. 熔炼	róngliàn	（动）	melt
21. 填塞	tiánsāi	（动）	fill in
22. 诛灭	zhūmiè	（动）	kill
23. 青虬	qīngqíu	（名）	black dragon
24. 缭绕	liáorǎo	（动）	curl up

十四、

1. 娇贵	jiāoguì	（形）	be indulged
2. 伴奏	bànzòu	（动）	accompany (with musical instruments)
3. 燕子	yànzi	（名）	swallow

194

4. 捕捉	bǔzhuō	（动）	catch
5. 罩	zhào	（动）	to cover
6. 色彩斑斓	sècǎi bānlán		colourful
7. 怀孕	huáiyùn	（动）	be pregnant
8. 胸膛	xiōngtáng	（名）	chest
9. 破裂	pòliè	（动）	open up

十五、

1. 妃子	fēizi	（名）	concubine
2. 踩	cǎi	（动）	step on
3. 拇指	mǔzhǐ	（名）	toe
4. 胎衣	tāiyī	（名）	afterbirth
5. 怪胎	guàitāi	（名）	a strange looking foetus
6. 不祥	bùxiáng	（形）	ominous
7. 狭窄	xiázhǎi	（形）	narrow
8. 小心翼翼	xiǎoxīn-yìyì		careful
9. 伐	fá	（动）	cut
10. 于心不忍	yú xīn bù rěn		take pity on
11. 覆盖	fùgài	（动）	to cover
12. 神秘	shénmì	（形）	mysterious
13. 不同凡响	bùtóng-fánxiǎng		very unusual or extraordinary
14. 抛弃	pāoqì	（动）	abandon
15. 始祖	shǐzǔ	（名）	ancestor
16. 农艺	nóngyì	（名）	agriculture
17. 擅长	shàncháng	（动）	be good at

十六、

1. 百般	bǎibān	（副）	in every possible way
2. 虫子	chóngzi	（名）	worm
3. 瓠	hù	（名）	gourd (bowl)
4. 五色斑斓	wǔsè bānlán		the colours of rainbow

5. 形影不离	xíngyǐng-bùlí		always together
6. 侵犯	qīnfàn	（动）	launch an attack
7. 骚扰	sāorǎo	（动）	harass
8. 残害	cánhài	（动）	cruelly kill
9. 忧心忡忡	yōuxīn chōngchōng		heavyhearted
10. 荒郊	huāngjiāo	（名）	wilderness
11. 旷野	kuàngyě	（名）	wilderness
12. 背弃	bèiqì	（动）	desert
13. 吉祥	jíxiáng	（形）	auspicious
14. 兆头	zhàotou	（名）	sign; omen
15. 锣鼓	luógǔ	（名）	drums and gongs
16. 彻夜	chèyè	（名）	all night
17. 酩酊大醉	mǐngdǐng dà zuì		be dead drunk
18. 帐篷	zhàngpéng	（名）	tent
19. 无精打采	wújīng-dǎcǎi		in low spirits
20. 自食其言	zì shí qí yán		go back on one's word
21. 魁梧	kuíwú	（形）	tall and strong
22. 峻拔	jùnbá	（形）	high and steep
23. 秀丽	xiùlì	（形）	beautiful
24. 密林	mìlín	（名）	dense forests
25. 溪	xī	（名）	stream
26. 潭	tán	（名）	tarn
27. 馥郁	fùyù	（形）	fragrant
28. 阻塞	zǔsè	（动）	block
29. 屁股	bìgu	（名）	bullocks; behind
30. 缠	chán	（动）	keep pestering
31. 崇拜	chóngbài	（动）	worship

十七、

1. 朱砂	zhūshā	（名）	cinnabar

196

2. 漆	qī	（名）	lacquer	
3. 避免	bìmiǎn	（动）	avert	
4. 角斗	juédòu	（动）	contest；wrestle	
5. 抛	pāo	（动）	throw	
6. 泥	ní	（名）	clay	
7. 雕镂	diāolòu	（动）	carve	
8. 稳当	wěndang	（形）	safe	
9. 拥戴	yōngdài	（动）	support，accept	
10. 和睦	hémù	（形）	harmony	
11. 兴旺	xīngwàng	（动）	prosperous	
12. 明眸皓齿	míngmóu-hàochǐ		having shining eyes and white teeth；comely	
13. 执着	zhízhuó	（形）	inflexible	
14. 痴迷	chīmí	（动）	infatuate	
15. 任性	rènxìng	（动）	wilful	
16. 误掉	wùdiào	（动）	miss	
17. 永恒	yǒnghéng	（形）	everlasting	
18. 坠落	zhuìluò	（动）	fall	
19. 凝视	níngshì	（动）	stare at	
20. 湍急	tuānjí	（形）	rapid	
21. 迁徙	qiānxǐ	（动）	move；migrate	
22. 诅咒	zǔzhòu	（动）	curse	
23. 霹雳	pīlì	（名）	a great explosion；thunderclap	
24. 茂密	màomì	（形）	dense；thick	
25. 禽兽	qínshòu	（名）	birds and beasts	
26. 忧伤	yōushāng	（动）	gloomy	

第二章

一、

1. 天廷	tiāntíng	（名）	celestial sky
2. 辅佐	fǔzuǒ	（动）	assist
3. 圆规	yuánguī	（名）	compass
4. 称杆	chènggǎn	（名）	scale;the arm of a steelyard
5. 曲尺	qūchǐ	（名）	carpenter's square
6. 称锤	chèngchuí	（名）	the sliding weight of a steelyard

二、

1. 吞没	tūnmò	（动）	swallow up
2. 叼	diāo	（动）	hold in the mouth

三、

1. 无道	wúdào	（形）	ruthless
2. 原野	yuányě	（名）	open country
3. 漂浮	piāofú	（动）	float
4. 凄惨	qīcǎn	（形）	miserable

四、

1. 蹄	tí	（名）	hoof
2. 强悍	qiánghàn	（形）	intrepid
3. 兴作	xīngzuò	（动）	stir up
4. 败仗	bàizhàng	（名）	defeat
5. 趁势	chènshì	（副）	take advantage of a favourable situation

五、

1. 猛志	měngzhì	（名）	fighting spirit

2. 埋葬	máizàng	（动）	bury
3. 肚脐	dùqí	（名）	navel
4. 盾牌	dùnpái	（名）	shield
5. 板斧	bǎnfǔ	（名）	broad axe

六、

1. 炽热	chìrè	（形）	red-hot
2. 烘烤	hōngkǎo	（动）	scorch
3. 烦燥	fánzào	（形）	irritable
4. 硕果	shuòguǒ	（名）	rich fruits
5. 累累	léiléi	（形）	clusters of

七、

1. 耀眼	yàoyǎn	（形）	dazzling
2. 撒	sǎ	（动）	scatter
3. 蒸烤	zhēngkǎo	（动）	scorch
4. 枯焦	kūjiāo	（动）	dry up
5. 心烦意乱	xīfán yìluàn		be terribly upset
6. 断绝	duànjué	（动）	run out of
7. 威胁	wēixié	（动）	threaten
8. 灾难	zāinàn	（名）	disaster
9. 祈求	qíqiú	（动）	pray for
10. 祷告	dǎogào	（动）	pray
11. 相映	xiāngyìng	（动）	contrast
12. 精魂	jīnghún	（名）	spirit
13. 吹灰之力	chuīhuīzhīlì		just a small effort
14. 制服	zhìfú	（动）	subdue
15. 祸害	huòhài	（名）	scourge；threat
16. 泽	zé	（名）	lake
17. 鸷鸟	zhìniǎo	（名）	birds of prey
18. 凶悍	xiōnghàn	（形）	fierce

19.	蟒	mǎng	（名）	python
20.	掀翻	xiānfān	（动）	upset
21.	囫囵	húlún	（名）	whole
22.	芯子	xìnzi	（名）	the forked tongue of a python or snake
23.	从容不迫	cōngróng-bùpò		calm and unhurried
24.	稀疏	xīshū	（形）	thin
25.	刚毛	gāngmáo	（名）	tough hair
26.	掘	jué	（动）	dig
27.	蠢	chǔn	（形）	foolish
28.	恩德	ēndé	（名）	favour; grace

八、

1.	滔天	tāotiān	（动）	dash to the skies
2.	淹	yān	（动）	to flood
3.	煎熬	jiān'áo	（动）	suffer
4.	栖息	qīxī	（动）	live; rest
5.	侵袭	qīnxí	（动）	hit
6.	罕见	hǎnjiàn	（形）	seldom seen
7.	刚强	gāngqiáng	（形）	strong-willed
8.	耿直	gěngzhí	（形）	upright
9.	果断	guǒduàn	（形）	decisive
10.	腐烂	fǔlàn	（动）	decay
11.	赐	cì	（动）	bestow on
12.	驮	tuó	（动）	carry on the back
13.	堙障	yīnzhàng	（动）	prevent, block
14.	疏导	shūdǎo	（动）	dredge
15.	功德	gōngdé	（名）	merits and virtues
16.	洞穴	dòngxué	（名）	cave

第三章

一、
1. 腾云驾雾   téngyún-jiàwù   mount the clouds and rid the mist
2. 缩小   suōxiǎo   （动）   make one shorter

二、
1. 灵巧   língqiǎo   （形）   delicate
2. 彬彬有礼   bīnbīn-yǒulǐ   urbane
3. 行礼   xínglǐ   （动）   bow；salute
4. 寿命   shòumìng   （名）   life-span

三、
1. 骨节   gǔjié   （名）   joint
2. 搀扶   chānfú   （动）   support sb. with one's hand

四、
1. 佩   pèi   （动）   carry
2. 顺从   shùncóng   （形）   obedient
3. 谦让   qiānràng   （动）   polite

五、
1. 盘绕   pánrào   （动）   entwine

六、
1. 后嗣   hòusì   （名）   descendant
2. 维持   wéichí   （动）   support；keep

七、
1. 迅疾   xùnjí   （形）   swift

八、

1. 鬣毛　　　　lièmáo　　　　（名）　　　mane
2. 机械　　　　jīxiè　　　　　（名）　　　machinery

九、

1. 怪异　　　　guàiyì　　　　（形）　　　strange

十一、

1. 趾　　　　　zhǐ　　　　　　（名）　　　toe

十二、

1. 丢弃　　　　diūqì　　　　　（动）　　　abandon；give up
2. 拐杖　　　　guǎizhàng　　　（名）　　　walking stick

十三、

1. 垂　　　　　chuí　　　　　　（动）　　　hang down
2. 垫席　　　　diànxí　　　　　（名）　　　mattress
3. 使唤　　　　shǐhuàn　　　　（动）　　　use；order about

十四、

1. 蝗虫　　　　huángchóng　　（名）　　　locust

十五、

1. 鼻孔　　　　bíkǒng　　　　（名）　　　nostril

十六、

1. 黍子　　　　shǔzi　　　　　（名）　　　broomcorn millet

十八、

1. 卵生　　　　luǎnshēng　　　（名）　　　oviparity
2. 凤凰　　　　fènghuáng　　　（名）　　　phoenix

二十、

1. 猕猴　　　　míhóu　　　　　（名）　　　macaque
2. 火炭　　　　huǒtàn　　　　（名）　　　charcoal
3. 粪便　　　　fènbiàn　　　　（名）　　　excrement

二十一、

1. 美饰　　　　měishì　　　　（名）　　　ornamentation

二十二、

1. 巡视　　xúnshì　　（动）　　make an inspection tour
2. 感叹　　gǎntàn　　（动）　　sigh with feeling
3. 敷　　　fū　　　　（动）　　pour；apply

二十四、

1. 晶莹透亮　jīngyíng tòuliàng　　as bright as crystal
2. 五脏六腑　wǔzàng liùfǔ　　the vital organs of the human body
3. 病灶　　bìngzào　　（名）　　focus（of infection）

第四章

一、

1. 辟　　　bì　　　　（动）　　get rid of，keep away
2. 妖邪之气　yāoxié zhī qì　　evil
3. 腋　　　yè　　　　（名）　　armpit
4. 蛰伏　　zhéfú　　（动）　　hibernate
5. 雷击　　léijī　　　（名）　　be struck by lightning
6. 狂病　　kuángbìng　（名）　　madness
7. 吠　　　fèi　　　　（动）　　bark
8. 痈疮　　yōngchuāng　（动）　　skin ulcer
9. 痴呆症　chīdāizhèng　（名）　　dementia
10. 旱灾　　hànzāi　　（名）　　drought
11. 肿痛　　zhǒngtòng　（名）　　painful swelling

二、

1. 韭菜　　jiǔcài　　（名）　　Chinese chive
2. 缘木而长　yuán mù ér zhǎng　　grow along the wood

3. 困惑	kùnhuò	（形）	puzzled；perplexed
4. 臭椿	chòuchūn	（名）	tree of heaven
5. 疥疮	jiècāng	（名）	scabies
6. 茎	jìng	（名）	stalk
7. 麻疯病	máfēngbìng	（名）	leprosy
8. 稻	dào	（名）	rice
9. 粟	sù	（名）	millet
10. 吐穗结实	tǔ suì jiē shí		sprout ears and bear fruits
11. 甲状腺	jiǎzhuàngxiàn		tyroid gland
12. 治愈	zhìyù	（动）	cure
13. 坏疽	huàijū	（名）	gangrene
14. 纹理	wénlǐ	（名）	grain；veins
15. 分泌	fēnmì	（动）	give out，secrete
16. 麦芽糖	màiyátáng	（名）	malt sugar；maltose
17. 顶饥	dǐng jī		get rid of hunger
18. 染	rǎn	（动）	dye
19. 木瓜	mùguā	（名）	Chinese flowering quince
20. 聋	lóng	（动）	deaf
21. 杨树	yángshù	（名）	poplar
22. 核	hé	（名）	kernel
23. 疟疾	nüèji	（名）	malaria
24. 涂	tú	（动）	smear
25. 驯服	xúnfú	（动）	tame
26. 制怒	zhì nù		control one's anger
27. 佐料	zuǒliào	（名）	condiments
28. 羹汤	gēngtāng	（名）	soup
29. 延年益寿	yánnián-yìshòu		prolong one's life

第五章

一、

1. 佳肴	jiāyáo	（名）	delicacies；delicious meals
2. 圣明	shèngmíng	（形）	sacred；sagacious

二、

1. 篝火	gōuhuǒ	（名）	bonfire
2. 简陋	jiǎnlòu	（形）	simple and crude
3. 迸发	bèngfā	（动）	burst forth
4. 钻木取火	zuānmù-qǔhuǒ		rub the tree to kindle fire

三、

1. 逍遥自在	xiāoyáo-zìzài		enjoy oneself greatly
2. 利害关系	lìhài guānxì		gains and losses；interests
3. 憎	zèng	（动）	hate
4. 恬淡	tiándàn	（形）	indifferent to fame or gain
5. 淳朴	chúnpǔ	（形）	honest；unsophisticated
6. 置之度外	zhìzhī-dùwài		give no thought to
7. 飘飘然	piāopiāorán		floating in the air
8. 雷霆	léitíng	（名）	thunderclap
9. 胡须	húxū	（名）	beard
10. 人寰	rénhuán	（名）	human beings
11. 畜养	xùyǎng	（动）	feed；raise
12. 结网	jiéwǎng		make a net
13. 琴瑟	qínsè	（名）	musical instruments

四、

1. 种植	zhòngzhí	（动）	to plant

2.	五谷	wǔgǔ	（名）	the five cereals；food crops
3.	汲取	jíqǔ	（动）	draw（water）
4.	泛起	fànqǐ		stir up
5.	波澜	bōlán	（名）	waves
6.	合理	hélǐ	（形）	rational
7.	禾稼	héjià	（名）	seedling
8.	肥沃	féiwò	（形）	rich，fertile
9.	稼穑	jiàsè	（名）	farming
10.	鞭	biān	（名）	whip
11.	放牧	fàngmù	（动）	herd
12.	充足	chōngzú	（形）	available；ample
13.	盛	chéng	（动）	contain；hold
14.	陶器	táoqì	（名）	pottery
15.	历法	lìfǎ	（名）	calendar

五、

1.	瘟疫	wēnyì	（名）	pestilence
2.	作祟	zuòsuì	（动）	(of ghosts) haunt
3.	魍魉	wǎngliǎng	（名）	demons and monsters
4.	迷惑	míhuò	（动）	puzzle；confuse
5.	吓唬	xiàhu	（动）	frighten
6.	驱逐	qūzhú	（动）	drive out
7.	神明	shénmíng	（名）	god

六、

1.	原料	yuánliào	（名）	raw material
2.	麻	má	（名）	hemp
3.	革	gé	（名）	leather
4.	印痕	yìhén	（名）	print；mark
5.	残片	cánpiàn	（名）	remnant
6.	音信	yīnxìn	（名）	news

206

7. 嘶叫	sījiào	（动）	neigh
8. 发誓	fāshì	（动）	make a promise
9. 挣脱	zhèngtuō	（动）	get rid of；throw off
10. 缰绳	jiāngshéng	（名）	reins
11. 久别重逢	jiǔ bié chóngféng		meet after a long separation
12. 悲喜交集	bēixǐ-jiāojí		grief and joy intermingled
13. 缘由	yuányóu	（名）	reason
14. 功劳	gōngláo	（名）	contribution
15. 作数	zuòshù	（动）	count
16. 怒不可遏	nùbùkě'è		boil with rage
17. 悔恨	huǐhèn	（动）	regret
18. 凌空而降	língkōng ér jiàng		fall from the sky
19. 仙嫔	xiānpín	（名）	immortal goddess

七、

1. 浮	fú	（动）	float
2. 桨	jiǎng	（名）	oar
3. 浩淼	hàomiǎo	（形）	boundless
4. 工艺	gōngyì	（名）	technology
5. 车轮	chēlún	（名）	wheel
6. 车辕	chēyuán	（名）	cart shafts
7. 脑海	nǎohǎi	（名）	mind
8. 图案	tú'àn	（名）	pattern；design
9. 自如	zìrú	（形）	smoothly；freely
10. 蒸汽机	zhēngqìjī	（名）	steam engine
11. 轨辙	guǐzhé	（名）	wheel tracks

八、

1. 媒妁	méishuò	（名）	matchmaker
2. 豢养	huànyǎng	（动）	keep
3. 圈	juàn	（名）	pen

4. 喂养	wèiyǎng	（动）	feed
5. 赶集	gǎnjí	（动）	go to market
6. 玉坠	yùzhuì	（名）	jade earring
7. 瓮	wèng	（名）	jar
8. 钵	bō	（名）	bowl
9. 瓦	wǎ	（名）	tile
10. 冶炼	yěliàn	（动）	smelt
11. 划时代	huàshídài	（形）	epoch-making
12. 鼎	dǐng	（名）	an ancient cooking vessel
13. 为非作歹	wéifēi-zuòdǎi		do evil
14. 毛骨悚然	máogǔ-sǒngrán		frighten
15. 刑具	xíngjù	（名）	tool of punishment
16. 繁缛	fánrù	（形）	overelaborate
17. 一去不复返	yī qù bù fù fǎn		gone for ever

九、

1. 超凡入圣	chāo fán rù shèng		sacred；sagacious
2. 磬	qìng	（名）	chime stone
3. 规矩	guījǔ	（名）	rule；standard
4. 准绳	zhǔnshéng	（名）	standard
5. 分辨	fēnbiàn	（动）	distinguish
6. 优劣	yōu-liè		good and bad
7. 总管	zǒngguǎn	（名）	manager；head of craftsmen

十、

1. 天文	tiānwén	（名）	astronomy
2. 耕耘	gēngyún	（动）	to plant；to cultivate

十一、

1. 是非曲直	shìfēi-qūzhí		rights and wrongs
2. 惊天动地	jīngtiān-dòngdì		earthshaking
3. 称雄	chēngxióng	（动）	become powerful

4. 潜入　　　　　qiánrù　　　　（动）　dive

十二、

1. 寻欢作乐　　xún huān zuò lè　　　to seek pleasure
2. 正统　　　　zhèngtǒng　　（形）　orthodox
3. 舆论　　　　yúlùn　　　　（名）　public opinion
4. 无拘无束　　wújū-wúshù　　　　　carefree
5. 通宵达旦　　tōngxiāo-dádàn　　　all night long
6. 山麓　　　　shānlù　　　　（名）　the foot of a mountain
7. 律调　　　　lǜdiào　　　　（名）　melody；tune
8. 雄　　　　　xióng　　　　（形）　male
9. 雌　　　　　cí　　　　　　（形）　female
10. 对垒　　　　duìlěi　　　　（动）　stand facing each other
11. 麋皮　　　　mípí　　　　　（名）　elk skin
12. 缶　　　　　fǒu　　　　　　（名）　vat
13. 粗犷　　　　cūguǎng　　　（形）　bold and unconstrained
14. 豪迈　　　　háomài　　　　（形）　heroic
15. 气势　　　　qìshì　　　　　（名）　momentum

十三、

1. 品味　　　　pǐnwèi　　　　（动）　to savour
2. 体察　　　　tǐchá　　　　　（动）　to feel；to experience
3. 仿效　　　　fǎngxiào　　　（动）　to imitate
4. 引吭高歌　　yǐnháng-gāogē　　　to sing joyfully in a loud voice
5. 频繁　　　　pínfán　　　　（形）　often
6. 军威大振　　jūnwēi dà zhèn　　　the might of the troops has been greatly boosted
7. 所向披靡　　suǒxiàng-pīmǐ　　　to sweep all obstacles away
8. 瘫软如泥　　tānruǎn rú ní　　　as weak and limp as mud
9. 妖魔鬼怪　　yāomó-guǐguài　　　demons，monsters and ghosts
10. 逃之夭夭　　táozhīyāoyāo　　　to make one's getaway

十四、

1. 灶　　　　zào　　　　　（名）　　kitchen range
2. 沧海　　　cānghǎi　　　（名）　　blue sea
3. 鬼魅　　　guǐmèi　　　 （名）　　evil ghost
4. 过失　　　guòshī　　　 （名）　　fault
5. 美味佳肴　měiwèi jiāyáo　　　　 delicious foods

（京）新登字 157 号

图书在版编目（CIP）数据

中国神话世界＝THE WORLD OF CHINESE MYTHS：
英文对照/陈家宁,杨阳编.—北京:北京语言学院出版社,1995
　ISBN 7-5619-0414-2

　Ⅰ.中…

　Ⅱ.①陈…②杨…

　Ⅲ.神话-中国

　Ⅳ.I276.5

书　　名：中国神话世界
作　　者：陈家宁　杨阳　编著
出　　版：北京语言学院出版社
印　　刷：北京市朝阳区北苑印刷厂
发　　行：中国国际图书贸易总公司
　　　　　中国北京车公庄西路 35 号
　　　　　邮政信箱：北京 399 号　邮政编码 100044
版　　次：（汉英）1995 年 9 月（20 开）1 版 1 次印刷
国图书号：7-CE-3063P
　　　　　03500